Walker's Way

How Are You Walking In Your Life?

Claudette Carter

Claudettecarter83@yahoo.com

Printed in the United States of America
ISBN 978-1-958434-77-2 (sc)
ISBN 978-1-958434-23-9 (e)

Library of Congress Control Number: 2022911119

2022.10.28

MainSpring Books
5901 W. Century Blvd
Suite 750
Los Angeles, CA, US, 90045

www.mainspringbooks.com

WALKER'S WAY

How are you walking through life? This compelling true story of love, courage, and humility was inspired by my husband Walker Lee Carter -- a man known to be prolific in his example before others. Walker excelled in sports and his teachings of true love was based on his faith in Jehovah God as he walked intently in the footsteps of Jesus Christ. Walker loved God's word in the Bible. Despite its imperfections, he still tried to apply it in his life on a daily basis and share the truths with others.

Walker's Way is not a book based on fairytales and fabrications of life. This powerful publication proves that courage is vital to avoid wars, hatred, and false teachings of men. "So, this is what I say and bear witness to in the Lord, that you should no longer go on walking just as the nations also walk, in the futility of their minds. They are in darkness mentally and alienated from the life that belongs to God, because of the ignorance that is in them, because of the insensitivity of their hearts." Ephesians 4:17-18 *(New World Translation of the Holy Scriptures)* Walker Carter studied those words and applied them as Jehovah God and Jesus Christ taught him to do. Walker would never wage war against his brother or sister regardless of their race or religious background. Scriptural application and the way he walked through life with a demonstration of true love was a necessity.

Walker was a stellar athlete. As an underprivileged boy who experienced racism, he defied all odds and became a beloved man that touched the hearts of so many regardless of their race even after his death. Gibson Ivery was a lifetime friend who played football and ran track with Walker who stated, "I appreciated I got to know him and play with him. Today, I wish I could be the man that Walker was. He was a gentleman indeed."

Walker's Way is an influential, biographical experience that reveals how a man who loved and served God walked through life as he gained love and respect from others. This book will capture the hearts of its readers as they cheer for Walker's victories as a young black man who never restricted his life based on the color of his skin. This inspired Walker to acknowledge others not as black or white but as individuals created by God that could excel to their greatest potential in life whether in sports or other activities.

Walker graduated in 1978 from Widener University in Chester, Pennsylvania. He excelled as an athlete, where he, along with teammates, coaches, and fans, went on to win the national championships in football as well as track and field during the 70s and 80s. Walker later became the first football black assistant coach to the award-winning head coach Bill Manlove at Widener. He also served as the first black assistant coach in track and field under head coach Bob Young.

Walker's Way is also premised on how he became employed by PECO which is a subsidiary of Exelon Corporation. Within this company, Walker worked as a First Class Lineman. He excelled and became admired by corporate leaders and thousands of other employees throughout the company. Walker's intense love for me as his wife, our two daughters, thousands of family members, and friends exemplified what a true human being he was. Although imperfect, he achieved so much in his lifetime. He lived his life as a team player who demonstrated spiritual leadership based on his love for God and people. This set the standard for the love, respect, and appreciation by others.

Over the years, millions of books have been published throughout the world. These books, based on the ISBN registration, have generated hundreds of billions of dollars. One of the most effective tools utilized by the devil is how people have been taught to resent God's name and the fact that his son is Jesus Christ. *Walker's Way* will stand-alone as one of the very few true-to-life stories that boldly uses God's name, which is Jehovah. Psalms 83:18 states, "That men may know that thou, whose name alone is JE-HO'VAH, art the most high over all the earth." *(The King James Version of the Holy Bible – Old and New Testament.))* When we view the Bible in its truthful form, the precious relationship that existed in heaven, possibly for billions of years between Almighty God and his son Jesus Christ, is revealed. If my focus for *Walker's Way* was for financial gain, I would never have included this powerful truth of how our Grand Creator Jehovah God sent his only begotten son Jesus Christ to the earth as the savior for all mankind. "Herein is love, not that we loved God, but that he loved us, and sent his Son, to be the propitiation for our sins." *(King James Version)* Based on what Walker believed after carefully studying the Bible, he taught others as well as our family this verifiable truth. These teachings based on God's thoughts from his word, the Bible, helped each of us survive and strive throughout this troubled world.

Over the years, Walker and I, as well as our daughters, have been confronted with death, sickness, pain, mental illness, and sorrow like billions of humans regardless of their race. Unless you are a robot, as human beings, we feel empathy for people. We want the very best for our worldwide neighbors. Every day on the news, we see vicious wars as brothers and sisters kill each other. We're all God's children, and this is painful. Consider carefully as well as prayerfully, why are Orthodox in Russia fighting and killing Orthodox in Ukraine? What religious leaders would allow this to occur if they based what they are teaching on the Bible? Regardless of your religious beliefs, God as well as his son Jesus Christ taught us to love one another. Are we disregarding these teachings and examples that Jesus set while on earth so that religious leaders can kill the truth once again? In the Holy Scriptures John 14:6, "Jesus said to him: 'I am the way and the truth and the life. No one comes to the Father except through me.'" (*The Kingdom Interlinear Translation of the Greek Scriptures)* To discover additional information of these prophetic events that are fulfilled daily, visit our Bible based website jw.org.

CONTENTS

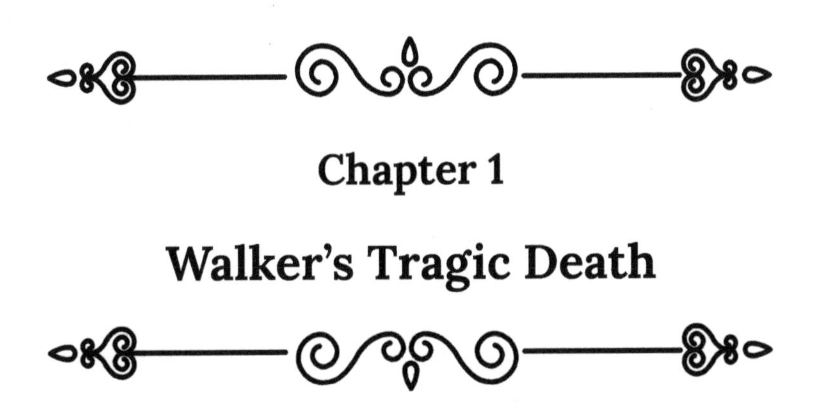

Chapter 1

Walker's Tragic Death

The Devastating Death of Walker Carter, a Beloved Husband, Father, Son, Brother, and Friend

On Wednesday morning, June 21, 2017, about 6:45 am., the sun cascaded through my bedroom window. My name is Claudette Carter, the wife of the deceased Walker "Baby" Carter. I could hear the birds chirping on that morning as I intensely wrote a letter regarding fraudulent activity by a company I dealt with. I was waiting for my hardworking husband, Walker, to return home after working a double shift at PECO Energy where he was employed as a First Class Lineman. Walker loved his job and the people he worked with. I was suddenly startled when the telephone rang and announced that it was Ocie Williams, my sister-in-law. Sounds of the birds faded out as I answered the telephone.

A few seconds went by as I apprehensively picked up the receiver. "Hello. Ocie, is mom, okay?" There is a dreadful silence from Ocie for the first few seconds. Ocie asked, "Has anyone called you?" "No." I said anxiously. I then asked again, "Is mom alright?" Ocie abruptly said, "I'll call you back," she hung up the telephone. I screamed into the receiver, "Hello. Hello." Suddenly, my doorbell rang twice. Then loud knocks on the door penetrated throughout my house. I rushed out of my bedroom and down the stairs. I could not imagine who would be at my door at this time and what was the urgency?

I cautiously peered out the stained-glass pane on my door. With hesitancy, I opened the door. I could not imagine as I asked myself, "Why was Walker's supervisor, Bob Fowler, on my porch with a State Trooper?" Tears started to overwhelm me as I screamed, "Bob, why are you here?" I backed up into my foyer as Bob and the State Trooper entered my home. I cried hysterically and screamed. Bob suddenly tried to comfort me with an embrace. In a downhearted voice, he explained, "I am so sorry. Walker died this morning." Desperately, I responded, "Are you saying that Walker is dead? This can't be true. I must be dreaming." I turned from Bob and called out for my daughter Jaleesa who was still asleep in her bedroom with the door closed. I was inconsolable and needed the pain within my heart to cease. I started to cry again frantically as I screamed, "Jaleesa! Jaleesa!" But there was no response from my daughter. I held onto the railing of the steps in my foyer as tears continued to flow. Thankfully, the State Trooper stood at the foot of the stairs and called out, "Jaleesa." His powerful masculine voice filled the house. Suddenly, Jaleesa's bedroom door flew open as she rushed down the steps. Without hesitation Jaleesa started to cry dreadfully as she embraced me. Jaleesa then asked, "Mom, what is it? Is it dad? No. No." She cried profusely before I could respond.

Bob stood sadly along with the State Trooper and continued to observe Claudette and Jaleesa as they both held each other. It was obvious both men felt the pain these women experienced. The agony of Walker's tragic death devastated Bob, corporate leader, co-workers as well as hundreds of linemen at PECO Energy.

I started to feel faint as I sat slowly on the third step from the bottom. Tears inundated my eyes until a headache consumed me. This caused me to reminisce about the day I met Walker. Our cherished memories were now just mine after he died. I dangled lifelessly with these memories. I envisioned Walker as he came down Chester High School's hallway. Yes, I wholeheartedly knew that due to our faith and Walker's faith, he wasn't literally there, but in Jehovah God's memory. In that source of comfort, I look forward to the hope that God will resurrect Walker in the future. Still, I required these flashbacks of our life to diminish the pain of his death. It gave me a sense of comfort as I meditated and then daydreamed about that intriguing day I met Walker Lee Carter.

Chapter 2

The First Time I Met Walker

I started to relive in my mind September 7, 1971. That was the first time I saw Walker in the hallway of Chester High School. My family had just moved from Mullins, South Carolina a few days before. I was an undefiled country girl full of excitement to be up north away from the tobacco and cotton fields. It was our first day of school. *Bernadette, my identical twin sister, and I had already gained a lot of attention upon our entrance of the school. We were dressed like twins with our white blouses, pin-striped blue jeans, and hair in afro puffs. The young ladies gazed with envy. I heard one of them say, "Who the heck are these girls? They got the nerve to be twins on top of that." Whistles came from the young men as they tried to determine who we were and where we came from. It was obvious to the young people that my sister and I were not from around these parts of Chester, Pennsylvania. Suddenly, a bell rang. Bernadette and I squeezed through the school courtyard. A young man opened a red squeaky door for us. We went up to the second floor into the hallway of Chester High.

Once we arrived on the second floor where our classes were held, this statuesque creature came through the doors. He was very handsome. I will never forget how Walker slowly breezed past my sister and me. Both of us were captivated by him although Bernadette tried to pretend he was not her type, since she liked tall, dark, and handsome boys. My mouth was slightly open as I became immediately infatuated with this young man. Yes. I was a country girl who liked tall, light complexioned, handsome young men. That was just my preference.

I can remember exactly what Walker wore. He had on blue jeans and a blue wind-breaker type jacket. When Walker passed us, he slightly looked my way as he continued down the hallway. I knew immediately this young man would be my husband one day. I started plotting as I reassured myself, "I got to find out his name. I got to check him out. He is fine." Bernadette and I stood against the wall plotting as I became the victor of this pursuit. Walker continued down the partially crowded hallway. I could see he was somewhat bow-legged which was one of the ultimate desires I wanted in my husband for the future. I could see us walking down the aisle. It was my dream.

Bernadette, abruptly, de-escalated that dream when she pulled my arm and said, "Come on girl. Let's go to class." Bernadette then spoke momma's famous words, "Stop thinking about that nasty, stinking boy and put your mind on your school lessons. Let's go" We continued down the hallway with attentive, whispers toward each other.

Our school transcripts were sent to Chester High beforehand. My twin sister and I, along with our twin brothers, were already registered to start classes. My brothers were Wardell and Wendell. They were a grade behind us. Each of us were excited to leave the fields of slave labor in the south. My mother Elease and my father Earlie had a total of 14 children. The last four of their children were two sets of twins. Bernadette and I were identical, and my brothers were fraternal twins. When my twin brothers were a year old, my father died. Bernadette and I were only two years old. At my father's death my mother Elease was left with 12 children. Two had died, my oldest sister Trina and Joseph who died as an infant. It was a tremendous tribulation for my mother as a widow of 12 children. My oldest brother later got married and moved to Chester. That was the start of our family's migration to the north from the south. Little did I know my family's move would have such a tremendous effect on my life and Walker's. I never imagined that first day I saw him that, we would love together, serve God together, live and experience our walk-through life together as husband and wife until his death. I thanked God that often in my life, I was clueless and just needed to learn how to rely on him to direct my life. I made so many mistakes that I learned from which made me the servant of God, woman, mother, and friend that I am today. After Walker's death, it was vital that I drew closer to Jehovah God and his son Jesus Christ to survive. Vicious attacks by mentally ill individuals were prevalent. I was thankful to God that he became my husbandly owner and protector now that I was a widow. I still appreciated and cherished the fact that I could linger at times about how I met Walker and the life we spent together. What a blessing those memories still are today.

Chapter Three

The Unforgettable Dance After an Annual Rivalry Football Game

We arrived at the Thanksgiving Day football game early in the morning. This was an annual event of a rivalry between St. James High and Chester High School. Residents of Chester showed up in record numbers. Both Chester High and St. James were in Chester. St. James was a local catholic school where most of its players were white. Of course, the majority of Chester High were black. The two different races caused the game to be hyped up even more.

I was excited because Walker played as a wide receiver on Chester's team. He looked adorable in his little black and orange uniform. There was very little I knew about football. I just wanted to see Walker make touchdowns. I wanted to scream, jump up and down along with the crowd in pure enthusiasm. That very day, Walker ran the ball in for a touchdown from Kevin who was the quarterback and his best friend. I was ecstatic as the crowd went crazy. Walker's touchdown helped Chester High win the game against St. James. Years later, after Walker's death, Kevin brought tears of laughter to my face. He explained, "We had this connection where Walker would know where to be on the football field so that he could catch the ball for a touchdown. Except on that Thanksgiving Day game where he was a little off because he had gotten high the night before the game, and he was still feeling the effects. He wasn't always the good guy." I laughed with Kevin in agreement because after we were married, Walker would get upset if he didn't have a good meal. There would be almost a hidden anger within him. That was part of his imperfection. Each of us have some type of problem that we must deal with.

After the game was over between St. James and Chester High, Walker was surrounded by his teammates as well as numerous fans who fled from the stands. There was an overwhelming source of excitement in the air. Walker finally walked out of the group and raised his helmet toward the bleachers. I wanted to imagine he was looking for me, although there was another girl there that I had heard Walker might be interested in.

I watched her from a distance to make sure she didn't try to approach him because I was ready to fight for that man. I felt a source of comfort because I knew I would see Walker at the Armory that night for our dance and celebration of Chester's victory over St. James.

The school dance and celebration that Chester won the game was on. I arrived with Bernadette around 7:30 p.m. The Armory was in downtown Chester. Loud R&B music played as we walked in. I can't remember what the song was because my only focus was to see Walker. Bernadette and I were dressed alike with our cute black jumpsuits and our hair in full afros. Bernadette leaned and whispered in my ear, "We are looking good. The guys are checking us out. I love being a twin because we get all this attention as the other girls hate on us." I could care less what my vain sister said. Sometimes I liked being a twin but sometimes I hated it because I thought Bernadette was crazy and prettier than I was, although we were supposed to be identical. She was always more aggressive and a troublemaker. Bernadette loved to tell people off as she would call it. Bernadette along with my youngest brother Wendell, who was a fraternal twin to Wardell, were the baby twins that would always speak their minds even to our mother Elease. Sometimes momma would just burst into tears.

Now that we had arrived at the dance, I became bored because I didn't see Walker. Suddenly, a boy named Chester Bird approached me with a big smile. He also played on the football team with Walker. Chester Bird was popular as well as a great dancer. He was somewhat of a show-off. Chester Bird was a rapper before rapping existed. He would go around school and as other students spoke, his response was, "Chester Bird, you got the word because the word is Chester Bird." What that meant I had no idea. He also had a terrible acne issue as most teenagers did at that time.

Chester Bird took me by the hand and asked me to dance. I hesitated as he insisted. We went out on the floor and started to dance. I tried to do a little robot and the bump. It was difficult. Chester Bird was the best male dancer in our school. He drew a crowd as usual, so I slowly backed away as my eyes searched for Walker.

Within minutes, the auditorium doors opened. The white quarterback Kevin Kessler walked in with Walker. Teenagers started to run toward Walker and Kevin. They gave them high-fives, hugs, and congratulated them for their victory over St. James High. The crowd left Chester Bird on the dance floor alone. Kevin and Walker looked the best out of all the guys in our class along with another guy named Michael Avarez who also played on the football team. Kevin was fine for a white boy, with his blonde shoulder length hair and baby-blue eyes. Walker and Kevin had been friends since they played football together at Smedley Junior High. Kevin served as the quarterback and Walker served as a wide receiver even in Junior High. Articles were written in the local newspaper about their great games and special friendship. I discovered the story about Kevin and Walker after my family and I moved to Chester. Eventually, I met this creature that I was intrigued by that God had designed specifically for me named Walker Carter. It was like reality met destiny.

Bernadette and I stood on the left side of Walker and Kevin as we checked them out. I whispered to my sister, "He's here. My baby is here." Bernadette laughed outspokenly and said, "Walker don't even know you're alive but for Kevin to be a white boy, he's kinda fine." Immediately, a Soul Train line was organized. Girls were on one side and the boys were on the other side. I ended up with Chester Bird as we did such dances as the camel walk, bus stop, funky chicken, the bump, popping and the robot. Cheers and shouts of joy filled the room as the teenagers enjoyed these dances. Once the song was complete and we stopped our Soul Train line, Walker came over to give Chester Bird a soulful handshake as he glanced at me. My knees buckled as I stood near Chester Bird. Walker was right in front of me as he said, "Man that was a good game you played today. Thanks for that block when I got the touchdown. Man, you played a great game. He quickly responded, "I'm Chester Bird, you got the word. The word is Chester Bird. But you're welcome, man. Kevin played a great game as well. He's cool and a dynamite quarterback." I stared hopelessly as Walker said, "I'll let Kevin know you said that." Chester Bird leaned in and whispered back to Walker, "Look man. Don't be checking out my girl. I'm dating Claudette, you can have the other twin." Walker discreetly whispered, "She's fine too, but naw man. It's cool. Go for it. Later, man." I felt my heart sink into my stomach as I overheard their conversation. I was not interested in Chester Bird. Anger grew within me. I was upset because I could have mustered up courage and spoke to Walker. I no longer wanted to dance with him. I was overwhelmed with disgust.

I went over to plead my case to Bernadette who was bored. "I can't believe Chester Bird kept me from Walker. I could have talked to or even danced with him." Bernadette looked at me with disdain, "Yeah. Right. Come on let's go to the bathroom." Bernadette grabbed my arm as she tried to force me to go with her. Bernadette released my arm and placed her hands on her hips. Disgusted, Bernadette screamed, "Are you crazy? That's Chester Bird. He may not be all that cute, but Chester Bird is popular, and he's got that sharp little orange and black mustang. Stop thinking about Walker and get it on with Chester Bird." I turned and walked away from her. I started to think about what Bernadette had said. I asked myself, "Was she right?" I returned to Chester Bird and tapped him on his shoulder. We started to get down on the dance floor. I could see Walker from a distance as he watched us dance. He looked disappointed. Within a few minutes, Walker and Kevin left the dance. I was devastated, but I pretended not to let this missed opportunity with Walker bother me. I must keep hope alive.

Chapter Four

Will I See Him at Our Senior Prom?

It was Chester High School's 1974 Senior Prom. I arrived with my date Leon along with my twin sister and her date Hunt. The event was held at the Downingtown Inn in Downingtown, Pennsylvania. We rode in Leon's black and red Buick. I looked forward to this event because I hoped and prayed Walker would be there. I wore a burgundy gown with silver gloves that came up to my elbows. Bernadette wore a pink gown with silver gloves as well. Unfortunately, we attended our prom with guys we didn't really like. Leon had his own car which was beneficial for us to get to the prom.

Both Bernadette and I worked full time jobs as inspectors at the Franklin Mint during our senior year in high school. We were able to have our gowns designed from sewing patterns. It was necessary that we dressed our very best because as disco queens, there was a certain reputation that we had to maintain. It was necessary that we had the nicest apartment and drive a sports car. I enjoyed racing men especially in my 280 Z. Bernadette and I loved to party, and our senior prom allowed us to enjoy another party and I planned to enjoy it.

Once we arrived at our senior prom, Leon grabbed my arm and said to Hunt, "Come on man. Let's take these girls inside and teach these young chicks how to party down." Hunt responded without hesitation, "I'm cool with dat." Bernadette and I laughed because both Leon and Hunt were a few years older, and we were convinced as I thought, "To be top disco queens that could dance all night, these old men didn't stand a chance."

When we arrived in the ballroom of the Downingtown Inn, I remembered it was decorated in our school colors of orange and black with streamers that cascaded from the ceiling. Orange and black tablecloths, black plates and silver flatware were nicely displayed. The decorations felt playful and frolicsome. Disco music played such as Eddie Kendricks' *Boogie Down.* Our classmates were dressed in their formal wear. Some of the young women had on beautifully colored evening gowns in rainbow shades. The male classmates were dressed in colorful tuxedoes with wide lapels and bare bottom pants. For once, most of my classmates looked nice. Unfortunately, I did not see Walker. We headed straight for our table which was in the back of the room. There was a certain amount of jealousy we received from other female classmates because Bernadette and I were identical twins and cute. They would call us, "Country girls," since our arrival from South Carolina three years ago. It was part of the bullying process, but Bernadette and I looked out for each other's backs.

I looked around the room and became disgusted because there was no Walker. I expressed with frustration, "This is a sad prom. Where are the football players? I need some excitement." Leon scoffed and boldly said, "Sister, you got me, a real man. Don't worry about no football players. Come on! Let's dance." Leon grabbed my hand and forced me to the dancefloor. Suddenly, I heard laughter as people clapped their hands and continued to dance. It was Walker and Kevin who came in with their dates. They both received high fives as classmates once again congratulated them. Walker had not only played football but also ran track and played basketball. He amazed people because of his athletic ability to play various sports. I heard that different scouts sought Walker to attend their universities because he was so talented.

I rushed toward the front of the room. I was desperate and I needed to say, "Hi." This would be one of the last times I would see Walker. Leon immediately followed me. With an envious tone, Leon waved his arms and said, "You are talking about those cornballs. Just because they played football, they're no big deal. Although Walker is kind of cool. Chester is proud of him. That boy is gonna be a professional football player one day. That's cool I guess." Walker was one of Chester's hopes for the future. People loved and admired him. Plus, Walker seemed to be a real nice young man. It was sad Leon and other people would say, "He's just one of those Jehovah's Witnesses and that's a cult." Leon had no idea that I loved Walker wholeheartedly and I didn't care about that. Walker did something right because he was talented, and Walker looked good.

Now that I had squeezed through the crowd, I had a better view of Walker, Kevin, and their dates. He looked a little corny with a blue, wide lapel tuxedo. I hated his date Karen who always seemed conceited. I decided in my mind, "Walker was too good for her. I realized nobody was good enough for him but me." It was so appropriate when Barry White's hit song entitled, *You're the First, the Last, My Everything* played. That song expressed exactly how I felt about Walker. Other classmates started to dance as Leon and I joined them. Bernadette also arrived on the dance floor with Hunt. Chester Bird had gained some of his groupies as he performed some of his wild dances. Chester Bird was such a show-off. I was glad my relationship with him had fizzled before prom night. Although I wasn't impressed with Leon either.

Bernadette danced next to me along with her date. She screamed "Come on girl. Let's party down. This is our senior prom." I screamed in response, "Whoa! Party! Party! We need to get down." I could see Kevin, the coolest, cutest white boy in the school, danced beside me with his date. I was thrilled to see that Walker danced next to Kevin with his date Karen. The night had progressed so tremendously. I could feel Walker looked in my direction. It was my hope and prayer that by some miracle he would ask me to dance. Our senior prom was almost over, and I never got to dance with Walker.

Leon stopped in the middle of our dance as the song entitled *Get Down* by James Brown played. I could tell he was frustrated and ready to leave. Leon finally asked with his arms folded, "Can we go so that we can head to Atlantic City?" We left that night to head for Atlantic City. It was a tradition for us to go directly there for Chester High students after the prom. I wondered if Walker and his date would come there as well. I know what Leon wanted, "Was to get it on with me. I hated that but I felt obligated. Bernadette and I had lied to our mother and told her, "We are going on a school trip with our counselor Miss Carey." My mother loved and trusted Miss Carey. We used that to our advantage.

The following Monday, after the prom, a miraculous event occurred. I came down the steps as Walker was on his way up the steps. I was so nervous that I dropped my book directly in front of him. Walker reached down quickly and picked it up. He handed it to me. We stared at each other for a few moments. It was as if no one else was around. I imagined Walker had lifted me up in his arms. It was just my imagination. Instantly, Walker smiled and asked, "Is this your book?" I stood there with a frozen smile of excitement. I could not budge. Walker looked at me with a confused and dumbfounded reaction. He handed my book to me and casually said, "Well, our high school days are almost over. I hope to see you again after graduation." Finally, I could move as I uttered the words, "That would be so cool. Thanks for picking up my book." I desperately needed these memorable minutes to continue. I stuttered and asked, "I heard that you might go to Widener University and play football?" My very life hung on any response given by Walker as he explained, "That's one of my options. I'll have to see. Good seeing you before graduation. Take care kid." I smiled and thought, "If he needed me to be childish like a kid, I would do that." Out of the corner of my eye I watched Walker as he strolled up the stairs. I hopelessly thought, "Wow! What a man!"

I could hear myself mumble words that were not coherent. "Okay. You know, I'm, I'm your biggest fan. I love you." Walker continued up the stairs. I'm not sure if he heard me. I wanted to scream out boldly and courageously. He had disappeared from my sight as the doors closed slowly behind Walker. I stood there like an idiot with my books pressed against my chest unable to move again. Finally, I realized the opportunity had come and gone once again without a kiss, embrace or a specific date that I could be with him. It was time to move on to my next class as I continued down the stairs. I arrived in class. Took my seat and started to daydream about my brief experience. I remembered how Walker's eyes met mine. The disquieting thought filled my brain, "Was this the young man I would marry one day? Would this dream become a reality? Only God in the heavens knew. But please, please let this come true." It was time for me to move on to reality.

Chapter 5

Our Unforgettable Graduation Day

The 1974 graduation of Chester High School was unforgettable. It was a beautiful sunny day at the Sun Center, located in Aston, Pennsylvania. Over 700 graduates sat in their caps and gowns. I was kind of proud and so was momma because out of those 700 graduates, I ranked 21 in the class. It was a major victory because I came from a segregated high school in the south. That year of 1974 was the first time Mullins High integrated. Our family moved that year to Chester.

There was a voluminous number of graduates which filled the center that day. The young male graduates of our class wore black robes and the young female graduates wore white ones. I had never seen such a large graduating class. In Mullins, South Carolina where I previously attended school, most of our graduating classes would be a little over 100. This was an impressive sight to see because I was on the same row with Bernadette and Walker as well. His last name was Carter and of course, my last name was Coleman. Every now and then I would glance down the row just to check Walker out. I knew this would possibly be the last time I would see him now that we had graduated.

After numerous speeches from our school principal Mr. Harold, the valedictorian, salutatorian, as well as some of our teachers and counselors, this special graduation day was about to end. It would become part of a lifetime memory that I would revisit in the future. The familiar song entitled, *Pomp and Circumstance* was played as we jumped to our feet and threw our caps into the air. This part of our lives in high school had concluded. Now it was time to infiltrate the real world and establish who I would become and how I would walk through life.

Amid the celebrations for our graduation, Walker looked slowly toward me. I mustered up the nerve to traipse toward him. Within my mind, I conjured that no one else was in the Sun Center because I could only see Walker. My amber eyes met his. I had to be embraced by Walker before leaving that day. I smiled as he reached for my hand and slowly enfolded me. My five-foot stature was consumed by Walker's six-foot, four inches stature to the point I was lifted heavenward. I envisioned the angelic melody *Hallelujah* filled the room. I do not want to let go because Walker was intensely involved as well in this embrace. Within my mind I screamed, "Don't let go. Let's stay here forever." He leisurely whispered, "You take care kid. I'll see you again." I grinned slightly and carefully kissed Walker on his right cheek. I glided slowly down his body as my feet touched the floor. After a few minutes, Walker released me. We gazed lovingly into each other's eyes. He smiled and let my hand go. I felt helpless and detached as I backed away. Other classmates gathered and celebrated around Walker.

I could feel Walker's watchful eyes upon me as other females hugged him. A feeling of disunity overcame me as the room appeared darker. I turned and winked my left eye at Walker before his face completely disappeared from my sight. It saddened me when all voices ceased. The graduation for Chester High's 1974 class had concluded. I asked myself, "Will I ever see Walker or any of my classmates again?" I felt dejected based on the pressure I experienced as each classmate had to encounter the real world. We were no longer children that depended on our parents but young men and women. Crestfallen experiences of life would befall each of us as well as joy and happiness. I prayed that each of us would receive more of the latter for the future.

Chapter 6

Walker Is an Amazing Football Player at Widener University

After we graduated, I lost complete contact with Walker. I knew he decided to attend Widener University here in the city of Chester where my family and I still resided. The only way I knew what he accomplished was through the local newspaper, *The Delaware County Daily Times.* I worked for a local attorney as a legal secretary. That part of my history I would rather forget because of the abuse I experienced as well as my twin sister. It was a job that gave me access to other political leaders who assisted me in my career. In the fall, after work around 6:00 p.m., I rushed across the street to the Legette's corner store. Walker played a football game against another local, rival Swarthmore College. I needed to know how his game developed. Once I obtained the newspaper, I ran upstairs to my old bedroom. Bernadette and I had gotten our own apartment, but we would come to visit our mother who still resided with my brother and his wife.

I started to read the article as I envisioned the announcer's explanation, "Widener opened on their 27-yard line where they fumbled the ball to Swarthmore on the 23rd yard line. Swarthmore threw a pass for 18 yards. On the fourth down, they scored a touchdown and created a lead of 6 to 0. Widener fans looked despaired and restless." My heart started to flutter. I wondered, "Did Widener lose the game?" Please God! No. I continued to read the article disillusioned with its content. The announcer described with intensity, "Wacky Jack Long is shown making a 40-yard sprint which caused Widener to take a 14 to 6 lead with 4:14 seconds remaining in the quarter. During the fourth quarter, a fourth down pass to Walker placed Widener on the 2-yard line. On his third attempt, Brady scores a touchdown, with the final score of 39 to 6. Widener fans rejoice over this victory."

After I read that, I leaped to my feet and shouted, "That's my baby!" Walker helped them get a touchdown and win the game. Widener slaughtered Swarthmore College 39 to 6. "You go baby!" Unannounced, my sister Bernadette appeared annoyed and envious,

"Are you crazy? Momma is gonna kill you. I heard you all the way downstairs." With tremendous excitement, I showed her the article and stated, "My baby did it. Walker helped Widener slaughter Swarthmore College." Bernadette grabbed the newspaper from my hand and continued to read the article as I danced back and forth. Disgusted with a loud scream she said, "Get a life! Walker didn't even run the touchdown in. He just got it to the two-yard line. Really, what's the big deal? You need to stop reading about him because Walker has moved on with his life. Girl, you need to do the same."

Once all this commotion had occurred, our mother Elease was also repulsed as she stood in the doorway of our bedroom. I immediately stopped my dances, dropped, and sat on the foot of the bed. Bernadette and I remained quiet as our mother stood in the doorway with her arms folded in disgust. Elease asked, "Which one of y'all screamed like a crazy person in my house?" Bernadette stood and pointed toward me immediately. She then turned and confronted our mother and disrespectfully said, "First of all, this ain't your house. This is Babee's so please be quiet. I got to deal with my crazy sister and mean mother." This brought a look of anguish in my mother's eyes. Bernadette and my youngest brother Wendell were the only children in our family that would tell my mother off and hurt her feelings to the point of tears. She then turned and started to scream and mock me as she said, "It's this idiot. She thinks she's in love with a guy who does not know she exists. Momma, please tell her to get a life and get over it. Your daughter is so lame." With tears in momma's eyes and arms still folded, she said, "Both of y'all better stop talking about boys and focus on keeping your jobs so you can take care of yourselves. Now, stop all this screaming and try to give me some peace and quiet. You can go back to your apartment and scream all you want." Elease turned and left the doorway. We continued to giggle as I danced.

Chapter 7

Widener's Televised National Championship Football Game

In December 1977, three years after our graduation from Chester High, Widener University had proven they were the very best in their division. They were featured on national television from Phenix City, Alabama against the Wabash Little Giants. I was thrilled for Widener because the entire Delaware Valley was excited that included Philadelphia, Pennsylvania. The game was broadcasted on *ABC Television Network.*

I had to work and was unable to attend Widener's championship game. Instead, I watched it on television in my apartment. By the time I turned the television on, the announcer said, "Hi, I'm Chris Lincoln here at the 1977 Division three NCAA Championship game. The teams once again are Widener Pioneers, out of Chester, Pennsylvania against Wabash Little Giants from Crawfordsville, Indiana. Wabash has a 10 to 0 lead over Widener." I was in a state of panic for Walker and Widener because there was only 34 seconds remaining in the first half. I became depressed for a few minutes.

I watched despondent as the announcer described how the quarterback Mark Walter of Widener Pioneers passed the football to Walker, a wide receiver on Widener's team. He took it to the 16-yard line, but it is marked at the 17-yard line. The announcer startled me when he screamed, "The excitement of the Widener fans is suddenly revealed. The fans are jumping up and down screaming. Coach Bill Manlove of Widener College is excited as well. With 26 seconds remaining on the clock, Widener takes a timeout trailing 10 to 7." The announcer retracted his statement and acknowledged, "Mark Walter, the quarterback for Widener reached the one-yard line." Quickly, the announcer said, "No. It's a touchdown! Walter did what Manlove said he does, nothing flashy. He just wins. Widener kicks the field goal, and it is good. The Pioneers lead 14 to 10. This drive for Widener was 68 yards in 7 plays. What a great game!" I was excited that Widener could win this game. It would have been great to be there to share this special time with Walker.

Another the announcer named Steve Davis started to give a little history of the Stagg Bowl Championship game as he explained, "A lot of people want to know how this game came about. Eight teams were selected by Division 3 from each region, East, West, North and South. These are the two teams that won."

The game was now a complete nail-biter as I nervously watched Wabash's quarterback throw a first down. With excitement, the announcer said, "Randy Melinger catches the football from quarterback Dave Harvey of Wabash. It's right on the money and the score is 16 to 14 putting Wabash in the lead. Division 3 games are just as exciting as Division 1 games." I could see from the television cameras that Wabash's fans were elated. The coach for Wabash paced on the sidelines. My stomach was in nervous knots as I watched my little colored television. I had learned a great deal of football terminology and how the game was played from my four brothers who loved the game.

The announcer Chris Lincoln said, "It is the end of the first half. With a touchdown from Quarterback Mark Walter, Widener fought back to the lead with 14 to Wabash's 10. Let's go down to Steve Davis as he interviews Coach Bill Manlove of Widener University." Coach Manlove looked cool as a cucumber when Steve asked, "Coach Manlove, the idea that you only had three plays in your offense. You kinda changed a flee flicker?" Without hesitation, Coach Manlove defended his actions and explained, "Well Steve, we kinda had to pull the tricks out of the bag at that time. It's a heck of a football game isn't it ..." Manlove refused to reveal too much of his strategies to win this game. Steve continued to investigate, "You got any new plans for the second half?" In a calm and determined voice, Manlove responded, "Just to come out with a basic game plan hopefully." I appreciated Coach Manlove's candor because it was time to go and win the game.

Reporter Steve Davis also interviewed the Coach for Wabash College Frank NeVaro. The Coach's demeanor was not as cool as Coach Manlove's. He attempted to make an excuse and stated, "We lost momentum. The quarterback for Widener is our competitor. We are gonna have to open up in this half." I started to feel a sense of victory for Widener because Coach NeVaro sounded as if Widener had already defeated them. I could now see that Widener would be victorious.

A particular song came into my head entitled, *Daydreaming and I'm Thinking of You.* I started to loudly sing these words, "Daydreaming and I'm thinking of you. I'm thinking of you as I daydreamed." Abruptly, Bernadette pushed the door open to my bedroom with her arms raised and shouted, "You can't be serious! How did you find out that Walker was playing in this game on television? I heard about this game, but I prayed you wouldn't hear about it." I quickly responded, "It's the talk of Chester. They are proud that Walker is a homeboy and is talented and black. So, be quiet because I'm watching the game. Please either leave me alone or watch Widener kick Wabash's butt." Bernadette was determined to share something negative, "What kind of name is that? Did you say the name of the team Widener is playing is called what?" Without a response I waved my right arm to get rid of my twin sister so that I could continue to give all my love and support for Walker. Bernadette's presence in the room hindered my joy. I screamed, "Please leave. Bye! Bye!" She refused to leave with arms folded and a smell of degradation, "You got like three boyfriends. One of them own a disco. Plus, you're a disco queen with her own ride and her own pad. Plus, you got your own money. So why are you still interested in what penniless Walker Carter is doing at Widener?" I completely ignored Bernadette and continued to watch the game. I knew those were not genuine compliments about me, but she had some selfish, self-centered motive. Finally, Bernadette revealed the truth, "Look! We got to get ready for the disco tonight. So please just get over it." Disgusted, Bernadette stormed out of the room and slammed the door. I screamed with joy, "Thank God she left. Now, it's just you and me baby. It's just you and me. Go Widener!" I was no longer interrupted by my sister's selfish insanity. I embraced myself with tears of joy. I looked heavenward and sang, "You are me and I am you. Now is the time. To say what is on my mind. I just need you in my life ..."

Questions started to enter my mind as I thought, "How will Walker deal with his fame if Widener wins this championship game? He didn't change with the championship wins in track and field earlier this year. When Walker returns home to Chester after being on national television, will all this recognition cause him to change?" I asked myself these questions nervously. There was no resolution in my head or heart.

It was the second half of Widener's championship game. I wanted to focus. It was now in the afternoon as the announcer loudly explained, "With 12 minutes and 31 seconds to play, Widener has the ball third down at eight. Keep in mind they must reach inside eighteen for a first down." The television camera pulled back and revealed quarterback Mark Walters as he threw the football to Walker for a touchdown. The crowd went wild as the announcer screamed, "Carter, with that great speed. He was so fast he had to stand and wait at about the third-yard line. Mark Walters threw this twenty-six-yard touchdown to Walker Carter with Widener College leading 33 to 28. What a play!" I was overwhelmed with excitement as I hollered, "Go baby! Alright. That's my baby." I could see Wabash's coach NeVaro as he paced back and forth on the sidelines.

With enthusiasm, the announcer proclaimed, "Walker Carter with 4.5 speed and he just outruns everybody." The camera shifted toward the scoreboard. There was 5:58 seconds that remained in the last quarter. The score was 33 to 28 with Widener in the lead. Unexpectedly, the announcer shouted, "Quarterback Mark Walters throws to Walker Carter. It's a touchdown again with 4:38 seconds remaining in the game. Widener now has an 11-point lead again. The score is now Widener 39, Wabash 28. That seventy-yard touchdown to Walker Carter from Mark Walters was amazing."

Within minutes, Wabash was shown going down the field as quarterback Dave Harvey threw a touchdown. They also scored two extra points which brought the score 39 to 36. Wabash was now 3 points less than Widener. My stomach knotted up again due to the intensity of this game. The announcer unfortunately started to summarize the game, "With less than a minute remaining in the game, the score is 39 for Widener and 36 for Wabash. This is the first time Widener is on network television. The alumni hall for Widener is watching this game on a seven-foot screen. With 29 seconds remaining Widener runs off one play. Widener is called for delay of game as Manlove tries to keep the clock running." I gazed intently at the television screen in a prayerful stance and screamed, "Come on baby. Y'all can do this. Let's go Widener. Let's go." The camera panned to Walker's parents along with Widener's fans as they celebrated.

The announcer felt assured enough to acknowledge, "Manlove won 36 games. Lost only four. This gives them eleven to one the longest winning streak to Division 3. Wabash gets the ball with 24 seconds left. Harvey, the quarterback for Wabash, throws the ball as the clock runs out. This is the final play of the season. It is caught and the Pioneers are Division 3 National Champions. Once again, Widener 39, Wabash 36." I leaped to my feet and shouted, "They won! Widener and my baby won. That's so cool. You go Widener. You go!" I was stimulated with pure joy as tears flowed down my cheeks. I clapped my hands together and said, "Congratulations, baby. I love you, Walker. I will always love you. I wish I was there to celebrate with you." Those words seemed empty and useless because at that time, Walker had no clue of my feelings for him. We were both living separate lives.

After Widener won the national championship game, a local reporter from Chester by the name of *David Brown who also worked with American Cablevision interviewed Walker. He was a source of pride for the City of Chester regardless of race or age. I watched the interview, and it was obvious Walker was humble and nervous. Reporter Brown said, "I have the privilege to interview Walker Carter, a wide receiver for Widener University, who along with his teammates, just won the NCAA National Championship Division 3 football game. Walker had two touchdowns in the final twelve minutes of the game. "Wow! How do you feel?" Drops of sweat consumed Walker's forehead as he responded with excitement, "This is cool. I just remember Chip Zawoiski told Coach Manlove, 'I'll see you in Alabama Coach.' Now we are here, and Widener won the National Championship game. I am so excited because of our team's determination both offensively and defensively. Our victory was a team effort."

News Reporter Brown was determined to catch Walker in a detached source of pride for his athletic abilities as he commented, "I appreciate your humility, but for our hometown fans, you led the Widener team in receptions with 38 yards and ten touchdowns during the season. Not only that, for this year and last year, you were named an NCAA All American in track and field as a member of the four by one hundred relay teams. That's impressive." Walker smiled nervously and explained, "Thanks for your research but remember that in 1975, there was a four by one hundred relay team such as Ron Hodge, Gary Foster, and Gibson Ivery who holds the Widener track and field record of 41.29. These are also some of Widener's most memorable athletes as well. Once again, it's always the team effort that is important."

Reporter Brown smiled as he cleared his throat and said, "Walker, thanks for the interview and for your consideration of your teammates. You really are an interesting guy that is quite humble. Congratulations again." Walker smiled and said, "Thanks again, but I learned what the Bible taught me at Proverbs 3:5-6 where I should never trust upon my own understanding but rely on Jehovah God to teach me how to love and support others who work just as hard as I do to create a team effort." Reporter Brown agreed, "Nicely said. You made your fans back in Chester along with Widener University proud today. Thanks again for the interview." Walker thanked David Brown as well as they departed.

Chapter 8

Our Encounter Four Years After the National Championship

Four years after I watched Walker play that outstanding nationally televised game, I lost count of his many touchdowns. Both of us pursued our own separate lives. I had created my own nonprofit television production company where I served as Executive Director. Bernadette and others helped me run the company. We interviewed various entertainers such as the Manhattans and numerous other groups and high-level politicians. The name of the company was Spotlight Productions, Inc. We produced an award-winning television show called *Delaware Valley Spotlight.* It had developed its own reputation as the show to watch to know what was going on in the area. I was tired from a show we had completed the night before because the next day I had to start at Widener University as an adult full-time student. I was exhausted until I entered my first English Literature class. It was as if the heavens had opened once again, and the angels sang *Hallelujah.* The last person I expected to see was Walker. I was elated. I looked around the classroom for an empty seat. There was a few on the right side of the room. Walker was on the left side surrounded by some of his football players. I heard that he was hired as the first black assistant football coach for Widener. Walker and I were the only black students in the classroom that day which did somewhat bother me, but he did not seem to be concerned at all. Walker had really become a source of pride as an athlete, coach, and man of his hometown and Widener.

I trembled as I walked to my seat. It was as if Walker watched my every step until I sat. I looked casually as Walker waved enthusiastically. I immediately responded as I waved back. We both acted childishly as Walker turned toward me. He screamed across the classroom, "What's up?! It's good to see you kid." My eyes sparkled just at the sound of Walker's voice. It had been almost four years since I watched his interview after the championship game. I hopelessly displayed this wide grin. All I could utter is, "It's good to see you as well."

Within a few minutes, Walker whispered something to one of his football players since he was now their coach. I saw Walker give the same player a unique handshake as if they had some sort of code. He then got up out of his seat and quickly moved toward my side of the classroom. My heart pounded as Walker came near me. He did not have any coolness about the way he walked but I loved this man, so whatever he did was wonderful to me. Walker's soft, brown eyes stimulated my very soul and gave me an interior and exterior glow. I escaped into a dreamlike state of ecstasy as I imagined Walker taking me by the hand gracefully and we began to slow dance. Our rhythm was perfect, and awe inspired by God as the angels watched from heaven. We continued to stare into each other's eyes. Before we could kiss, our English Professor said, "Welcome everyone. It's time to start our first class of English Literature for this semester." I was sadly forced to leave my beautiful dream.

Yes, Walker sat only a few feet from me. I escaped into another dream state when I heard his heartbeat as it beat in harmony with mine. He took my right hand defiantly while the professor continued to describe what the class was about. Walker's voice soothed my very being. He then said, "I've seen you on television. Congratulations on the success of your production company." Walker had obviously followed my career as well, which I appreciated. I wanted to humbly encourage him as well and said, "Thanks. I would love to interview you. Can I talk to you about that after class?" With total enthusiasm, Walker responded, "Sure! No problem. I'll give you my contact information after class." I nodded my head in agreement. We both turned in our chair from each other and directed our attention toward the professor as she proceeded with the class.

I started to date Walker that very day after our first encounter in English Literature class. He invited me to his house where he stayed with his sister-in-law Addie. I was a little confused as to why Walker lived with her. He later explained that with his Assistant Coach's, salary it was difficult to maintain his own apartment. Walker also felt a certain responsibility toward his sister-in-law because his brother Nathaniel was Addie's husband. He was pushed in front of a train and killed tragically. Some tried to say it was suicide, but Walker never believed that. He explained how Nathaniel had a wonderful life with his wife Addie and he had no reason to kill himself. It was later discovered that some person with mental issues had committed a similar crime to push people randomly in front of trains. This person was never prosecuted for Nathaniel's murder. Walker took Nathaniel's death hard because there was no justice for his brother's murder. I tried to understand the importance of why Walker felt he should be there for Addie.

Four months later in December 1981, Walker and I were still dating, but we had grown apart because my sister Bernadette and others told me I could do better. My heart told me it didn't matter that he was not in a position financially to marry me. I loved this man and that was all that mattered.

Widener had once again gone to the national championship in Phenix City, Alabama. He was now an Assistant Coach for the team under the behest of Bill Manlove. Widener once again won their division and went to the national championship in Phenix City. It was televised, and I made the horrible decision not to travel to see the game and support my man. Instead, I had to work so I was unable to attend. I stood in front of my colored television as I prayed for every movement of this game.

Chapter 9

Widener's Second National Championship and First Black Coach

I stood back at my apartment agitated because Walker was the first black Assistant Coach for Widener University. I should have been there to support him. He, once again, along with the coaches, players, and staff returned to Phenix City for another national championship game. Widener had become a source of pride for our entire area. I was thrilled to hear some of his family and friends attended the game to give Walker support along with the university.

The announcers Verne Lundquist along with Thom Gatewood said, "We are at the 1981 NCAA Division 3 Championship game featuring Widener Pioneers and Dayton Flyers. Culminating a search that began with 181 teams, these teams appear to be evenly matched." Thom Gatewood chimed in with this comment, "Widener and Dayton are evenly matched both offensively and defensively as far as giving up points and scoring points. They are in the same category. The key in the game could be turnovers. Widener Pioneers with Head Coach Bill Manlove is in the 13th year and they ranked number one in NCAA Division 3. Mike Kelly is Head Coach for Dayton Flyers." The game started as I paced back and forth. Paranoia consumed my thoughts, "What if Widener loses this game that is being televised nationwide? Walker would be devastated."

I started to bite my nails as one of the announcers screamed with excitement, "Mark Stephens kicks the ball as Tony Britton catches it. He's got it and made a touchdown. The score is now Widener 14 to Dayton's 10 with 6 minutes and 26 seconds remaining in the game." Time passed at a fast pace which I felt was positive due to my anxiety.

Announcer Lundquist described as he shouted, "Mark Stephens kicks the ball for three extra points and it's good! The score is now 17 Widener to Dayton's 10 points with 1 minute 25 seconds in the game. Widener scored 17 unanswered points in the 2nd half." I was elated as I jumped up and down. Adrenaline flowed throughout my body. Announcer Thom Gatewood joked, "It is 4th down at 21. Widener prep band sings goodbye. Widener is 37 seconds from getting the victory. Dayton's Coach Kelly is putting his headset back on. Don't know what kind of conversation he could be having maybe upstairs beyond this stadium." I laughed nervously at the joke.

My hands were clutched together as the intensity of Widener's victory seemed inevitable. Verne Lundquist announced with excitement, "Bill Manlove will go out with a championship ring in his 13th year." The camera panned and showed Coach Manlove shaking the hand of Dayton's Coach Mike Kelly. Finally, I felt relieved, and I could breathe. I unclutched my hands and rejoiced. Lavished with praise for their team, I saw Walker along with other coaches and players lift Manlove up on their shoulders as they celebrated. Announcer Lundquist screamed, "Look at that shot! Bill Manlove and Widener Pioneers are the 1981 Division 3 Champions. The trophy presentation is forthcoming with Thom Gatewood and Bill Manlove down on the field."

I stood most of the game due to pure excitement. I finally sat slowly in my bed with my hands in a prayerful position. Tears rolled down my face as Thom Gatewood questioned Coach Manlove. He asked, "How do you feel?" "Overjoyed," Manlove responded. "It was a great victory for a group of guys. We were certainly blessed this season." I stood up again and started to dance as I celebrated Widener's victory. I was now even more inspired as I said loudly to myself, "I must set up an interview with Walker as the first black Assistant Coach at Widener. This is a perfect excuse now that their team has won a national championship again. Alright baby!" I became breathless. I quickly sat down to regain my composure.

Chapter 10

My Interview with Walker After the Championship Game

After the championship game, I called the television studio to set up an appointment for Walker's interview. It was vital I maintained my professionalism when I spoke to my supervisor named Rhoda. She knew that I had feelings for Walker because I told Rhoda about him previously. I thought carefully how I had to mask my true feelings of love for Walker. My heart was still torn because of his family's religious beliefs as Jehovah's Witnesses. I often contemplated and asked myself, "Would he want me to one day serve Jehovah as well? Do I really want to marry a man who is not financially stable? Would my heart betray the realities of life?" I knew Walker could not afford to get married or have a family with me at the time. I scheduled the appointment with my supervisor for his interview upon his return from Alabama. Rhoda was ecstatic because Walker was viewed as a local hero, and this would boost our television ratings.

A few days later, Walker agreed to do the interview. He arrived a half an hour early at our studio in Wallingford, Pennsylvania. It was obvious he was anxious to see me. I watched Walker from behind a black screen that separated the camera crew from the editing staff. I could see that he picked at his nails nervously. Bernadette walked in the studio where Walker was before I did. She shook his hand and arrogantly screamed toward me as I hid behind the curtain, "Miss Executive Producer and host, it's time to get started. Walker, I appreciate that you patiently waited for my sister." He quickly replied in my defense. "I'm cool. I can wait for her. It's no problem." I rushed out before Bernadette revealed something that I did not want him to know. Bernadette was not only a bully, but she always had to speak her mind to let others know what she thought of them. That was just who she was. When I entered the studio, Walker got up immediately and embraced me. His tall stature enveloped me once again which I didn't mind. I really did miss Walker.

While Walker embraced me, I closed my eyes as poetic thoughts filled my head. I remembered our last night together before he left for the national championship game.

We were at my apartment in bed together. I reminisced poetically as my head laid upon Walker's chest. My heart raced as my fingers travelled through the hairs on his voluptuous chest. These words penetrated my thoughts:

"Upon His Chest, Soothingly I abide.
Love entangles my heart.
No utterances shared. Awake I cannot be?
Flashes of salvation fill my head.
Only death could pluck me from the midst of pure ecstasy.
If expiration is inevitable, please let this be my burial place?"

Walker remained quietly asleep as tears filled my eyes. I continued to stroke his chest. With each warm breath from Walker's nostrils, I became uncertain over the choices I would make. He would leave the next day for the game in Alabama. Within my heart, I had decided not to see Walker anymore. We were just too different. I had worked so hard for my material accomplishments. Walker was doing okay as an Assistant Coach at Widener, but his income was not enough for us to get married and build a family together. Plus, I didn't like his family's religious beliefs. I decided to move on.

Reality came to the forefront. I was back in the Wallingford studio with Walker. I was nervous because he now encircled me tenderly. Walker whispered in my ear, "I love and miss you, baby." Upon Walker's release, I exhaled. It was time to start the interview. Bernadette jumped up out of her chair and walked away. She critically then asked, "You sure you want to do this?" I sat slowly in my chair beside Walker. I never responded to what Bernadette asked. I turned toward him and said, "I got this. Baby, I need and missed you so much. Let's get this interview over and go back to my apartment." Walker reached for my hand as he reassured me, "That sounds great. Let's do this."

The camera pulled back and revealed Walker and me in our studio chairs as I spoke into the camera. I was nervous as he watched me introduce him to our viewers. I uneasily expressed, "Hi, I'm Claudette Coleman, your host for *Delaware Valley Spotlight.* Today, I have the immense privilege to interview the City of Chester's beloved, local hero, and homeboy Walker Carter. He just returned from Phenix City, Alabama where Widener University won their second NCAA Division 3 National Football Championship. Walker, thanks for joining us and congratulations on Widener's victory. He responded, "Claudette, thanks for inviting me on your show." I beamed as I leaned towards Walker and explained, "You graduated from Chester High, went on to Widener University where one news article stated that you became an outstanding performer for the Pioneer football team that won the MAC Championship in 1975 and 1977 making a semi-final run in the NCAA playoffs in 1975 and then achieving Widener's first NCAA Division 3 Football National Championship in 1977. Wow! You have been busy. How does it make you feel when you think about all these accomplishments?"

Walker now appeared to be more relaxed as he stated, "I was thankful to be a part of such a great team as a wide receiver on Widener's team during those championship games. It was truly a great team effort under Coach Bill Manlove along with the coaching staff." I laughed and mentioned, "I have been warned that you are quite humble as you give credit to your whole team. That's commendable. But Walker, Chester residents are proud of you also because you are the first black coach at Widener in football and track. How does that make you feel?"

Walker sat quietly for a few seconds before he responded, "Thanks to my God Jehovah, I don't really focus on the color of people, but I try to show love toward all races. Over the years, that has helped me to become a better player and coach." I was a little disturbed that Walker mentioned his God's name. I felt uncomfortable as I said, "Nicely explained. Recently, as an assistant coach for Widener, your team won the Division 3 NCAA Championship again for 1981. It was good to see the championship games nationally televised so Chester residents could see them. That's something you should be proud of."

Walker nervously leaned toward me and stated, "Again, it was a team effort. We have a great coaching staff and players like Mark Walters and running back Chip Zawoiski who helped us gain that victory. Coach Bill and all the coaches worked hard as well." I started to feel a little annoyed as I expressed, "Walker, I appreciate your humility, but you also excelled not only as a wide receiver but a sprinter and two-time All American in the 400-meter relay in Men's Track and Field at Widener. How did that make you feel?" It was clear Walker wanted to avoid too many compliments, but I just wasn't sure why? With a certain boldness he explained, "I give thanks to Jehovah for all those abilities because he created me. I just enjoyed playing with my teammates and now coaching. I am thankful for that."

I was now really confused as the camera moved in for a closeup. I immediately considered Walker's response and said to myself, "It was obvious to me that Walker planned to become a Jehovah's Witness." I now wanted to trap him with a question during the interview. I smiled nervously and asked, "Walker, it is imperative that you set an example for members of the black community. After you graduated from Widener, you tried out for the Buffalo Bills. You are also the first black person to coach football and track at Widener, therefore, you can't just think about your religious beliefs, but you must set an example for young black men in the community. Do you agree? I could now tell that question made Walker very uncomfortable as the camera moved in closer for a head shot. Walker shrugged his shoulders and said, "I'm not sure what my religious beliefs have to do with me setting an example for just young black men? Although I am not a baptized servant of Jehovah God, I have learned from the Bible that God is not partial, and neither is his son Jesus Christ. It is my determination to set an example for all humans regardless of their race or religious background."

I was now completely aggravated as Walker spoke so boldly about his religious beliefs. I decided and avoided eye contact with him so that he would not see how upset I was. I became passive and disengaged as the camera pulled back for my opinion. I was frustrated and disgusted that his response might cause me to lose audience members. I was terrified that Walker talked about what people believed was a cult although there was still no proof of that. I replied and rushed to close the interview, "That's an interesting perspective. I want to thank you for appearing on our show. Have a good day." I was angry and never waited for his response.

I was up and out of my chair as the camera faded to black. Walker jumped up as well. He reached for my hand. I lingered for a few seconds and abruptly pulled away. I refused to look at Walker as I cried, "I can't do this. I must go. My love for you is strong but my family will never approve of you if you became a Jehovah's Witness. I need their love, support, and approval as well as my fans and friends." I turned toward Walker as I saw the tears in his eyes. Walker pleaded, "Don't do this. Don't run again. I love you and I need you." With tears in my eyes, I was determined to escape. I felt like a wounded animal as my heart pounded. I threw both of my hands in the air as I screamed, "No. No. I can't do this."

I left the studio after Walker's interview was over. I felt defeated as I self-loathed my decision. I had once again run from the man that I loved. For the next few years, I continued to run Spotlight Productions as its Executive Producer and host along with my twin sister and nieces Kasia and Carol. I continued as a single disco queen. Every Friday and Saturday, Bernadette and I would be at the *Fox Trap, Whispers,* or other popular discos in the Philadelphia area. Sometimes, I would see Walker at some of the discos. I avoided any contact with him.

I continued to attend Widener as a full-time adult student. I would sometimes see Walker as he coached track. I felt a sense of pride for what Walker had accomplished as a coach for Widener. He had also returned to Widener as a student. Walker needed a few classes for his Business Management degree. I had only one art class with Walker other than the English Literature class my first semester at Widener. I sat on the opposite side of the classroom so that there was distance between us. I watched as our professor flirted with Walker because he was handsome, very talented and her favorite student. Walker was well-liked by everyone on campus. I often heard the descriptive words, "He's just a really nice guy." I knew that about Walker as well, but I wanted to please others.

I hated that he wanted to eventually become a baptized Jehovah's Witness. I fled and distanced myself because of his God. Family members disliked the witnesses. Some religious leaders described to their members that Jehovah's Witness were, "A cult that didn't believe in Jesus Christ." I knew that wasn't true because I heard Walker talk about Jesus. Members of my family which included my mother Elease did not like the witnesses because my brother Buddy married one. He was later injured in a car accident while Buddy was on his way back home to Connecticut from South Carolina. He refused blood as a Jehovah's Witness. Some of our family blamed his religion when Buddy died after a few days due to the accident. I respected Buddy's decision not to take blood. He quoted to our family Genesis 9:4 based on the *King James Version,* "But flesh with the life thereof, which is the blood thereof, shall ye not eat." Buddy stood firm for what he believed based on what the Bible said. He chose God over what our family thought. I respected that. In some ways I wanted to know more about this hated religion and why it was hated by so many. Why one of my friends told me, "I don't care what religion you join as long as it's not Jehovah's Witnesses."

Chapter 11

My Awesome Graduation Day at Widener

I graduated from Widener University in June 1985. Classmates of different races with caps and gowns surrounded me. I worked diligently to receive my Bachelor of Arts degree as a 30-year-old adult student. The President of Widener University was Robert Bruce. From the podium, he gave an inspirational speech. At the end of that speech, President Bruce said, "Congratulations to the graduates of Widener University's Class of 1985." Immediately after that statement, caps were anxiously thrown into the air with screams of celebration. I was thankful that the ceremony was over as members of my family joined me for this special day. I appreciated the hugs and congrats.

A downhearted feeling suddenly came over me even as others celebrated. I was in denial that the man I loved was not here to share this experience with me. I never anticipated as I looked through the crowd, but there he was. Walker eagerly came toward me with a determined stare. I never removed my eyes from his. Walker lifted me up. His embrace soothed my very soul as he whispered, "Congratulations baby! I missed you." God had once again answered my prayers. He swept me off my feet and held me in his arms. We peered into each other's eyes as I expressed, "I missed you so much. What's going on with you?" Before Walker responded, I confessed, "Walker, I love you. I don't care what other people think. I need you." He smiled and said, "I miss you so much and I love you too. Can we try this again?" Walker kissed me tenderly. I felt cherished and protected. My classmates, family and friends became nonexistent. It was just the two of us and nothing else or no one mattered. Some of my family asked, "Who is this man?" Bernadette screamed, "This is that Jehovah's Witness that Claudette is so crazy about. I told my family that she's got issues." Our kiss ended. I remained in Walker's arms as he carried me away from the confusion. I knew that Walker was the man I wanted to date and eventually marry regardless of what others thought.

After I graduated from Widener, life was great. Walker and I had gotten back together. I was hired as a Public Information Specialist for Upper Merion Township. I loved my job because it paid well. This job allowed me to meet and work with different people of all races. There were also numerous handsome men that I became friends with. I was the only black woman in the boardroom while I was employed there. I continued to serve as Executive Director and host in the evenings for Spotlight Productions. My life was awesome now that I had Walker back in it again.

While I worked at Upper Merion, Walker would come to my job. We would go out to dinner with some of the guys that worked with me. My co-workers loved Walker. They would often say the same cliché, "He's a really nice guy."

Walker still served as Assistant Coach at Widener for track and football. We were the "It" black couple who attended many football and track banquets. We would have dinner at one of the football coach's restaurants in Philadelphia. In some instances, we were the only black people in the entire room. Whether it was dinner parties at Coach Manlove's house with other coaching staff or wedding ceremonies for couples who worked for Widener or the Upper Merion Township staff. It never seemed to bother Walker because he didn't look at their race but saw them as people. I still had some adjustments to do with my beliefs as a southern girl. I appreciated that Walker made me comfortable as I watched how he reacted to individuals. We had become a couple that people enjoyed being around. Walker discreetly taught me his way based on the Bible with regards to how people should be treated and respected. I was intrigued that I not only loved this man, but I appreciated his temperament.

Chapter 12

Our Lives Were About to Change Forever

March 1986 changed our lives forever. I was exhausted most of the time. I assumed it was the 45 minutes to an hour that I drove every day to my job in Upper Merion. Early one morning, before sunlight penetrated through our bedroom window, I started to feel nauseated. I jumped out of bed and ran to the bathroom. I propelled everything in my stomach due to morning sickness.

Walker rushed to the bathroom door and with a slight grin he asked, "Baby, are you okay?" I sat on the cold bathroom floor as he beamed and asked, "Am I gonna be your baby's daddy? I've been watching you eat like a pig then throw it up. Come on kid. Tell me the truth? I jumped up off the floor and rushed past him. I sat on the side of the bed disgusted as I blurted, "Walker Carter, I'm pregnant. We are having a baby. I wanted to tell you at a better time." I would always use his full name whenever I was upset with Walker. "This is not a good time for me to be pregnant. I've only been on the job less than a year. What are we going to do?" Walker rushed, kneeled beside me, and grabbed my hand. He smiled and reassured me, "It's alright. We will work through this. I start my job at PECO next week. I'll be able to take care of you and our baby. I know what we can do. Let's get married." Walker dropped to one knee and asked, "Woman, will you marry me?" I hesitated for a minute and thought, "This is not the wedding proposal I envisioned." I turned and looked into Walker's eyes and screamed, "Yes. Baby. I will marry you because I love you. This is so unromantic." He kissed me, bounced to his feet, danced as Walker waived his hands in the air. I had never seen him so happy. I shook my head and laughed.

It was one of the happiest days of our lives. Walker would start his new job at PECO which a friend of my family, Ike Jones, helped him obtain. We were excited as we planned our wedding four months later and I would be four months pregnant. I was thrilled to be pregnant and to marry the man I loved. Walker and I had great love and respect for each other thanks to his God Jehovah.

While I was about a month and a half pregnant and planning our wedding, I was offered a major short-term job. At the time, State Representative Robert Wright asked me to serve as Delaware County Coordinator for *Hands Across America*. I would have to organize over 17,000 people to hold hands from one end of Delaware County to the other. This would help us raise money for the hungry and homeless throughout the world. I felt privileged as major entertainers created a song entitled, *We Are the World.* Diana Ross, Michael Jackson, Bruce Springsteen, and numerous others sang this song and promoted this concept. This was a great opportunity, but I still worked for Upper Merion full-time. I had morning sickness daily. I still worked with Spotlight as well. I had three jobs at the time. To fulfill this role as county coordinator, I left my job in Upper Merion. Walker was happy because he could see It was just too difficult for me.

On Sunday, May 26, 1986, I lined up with people of all races. They held hands to raise funds for *Hands Across America*. Newspaper articles were written about me if I would be able to accomplish this Goliath-like project. The day came and everything turned out successful. Over 17,000 attended and a couple of people were married on the line. My sister Bernadette, nieces Kasia, Carol, and brother Wardell were a major help. Walker pitched in with the camera crew as he worked with our cameraman David Brown. We interviewed Representative Wright, his wife and many other people that attended this *Hands Across America* event. I turned toward the camera that Walker held. Filled with confidence, I looked into the camera and said, "Today, May 26, 1986, we are witnessing thousands of people gathered to create a human chain to raise more than $100,000,000 dollars from coast to coast for the hungry and homeless. What a successful event this is as millions join us throughout the country even to the White House. President Reagan and his wife joined us in this effort where more than 6.5 million people held hands for fifteen minutes to form a continuous human chain across the United States. What a momentous occasion."

Walker peered and smiled from behind the television camera as I completed my interviews. I appreciated what he had done because it took a lot out of Walker to help me with *Hands Across America*. He previously explained to me, "It was only Jehovah God's Kingdom with his son Jesus Christ ruling as King that could solve the problems of the world such as hunger and homelessness." I had started studying the Bible with Walker's parents so that I could understand some of their points. I still had a lot of spiritual growing to do. I was thankful to God that Walker's parents, Susie and Walker, were patient with me because I was still clueless about so many things in life. I carefully considered that it was time for me to grow up because I was becoming a wife and mother within the next few months. Reality knocked hard at my door.

I held my stomach as the embryo moved inside of me. Walker came over with genuine concern. I felt tired and overwhelmed as I sat down. The crew from Spotlight took over and interviewed local businesspeople, politicians, celebrities, and residents that helped this event be successful. I was proud to see Bernadette as she interviewed Representative Robert Wright. With a smile, Bernadette ended it and said, "We would like to thank you for allowing our show *Delaware Valley Spotlight* to be a part of this encouraging event. It was a tremendous success." He smiled and stated, "No problem. We appreciate the hard work by your sister serving as coordinator and the staff of Spotlight assisting her. I think everything turned out successfully as well. Thanks again." I smiled and thanked our crew and staff as I the day came to a finality.

The day after *Hands Across America* concluded, major newspaper articles were written about the success of the event. My name as coordinator or the Spotlight crew were barely mentioned. We were a black television production company that served our communities. I knew that if things turned out successful, everyone, but Spotlight Productions would receive the credit. I was thankful that Representative Wright believed in me enough to do the job as coordinator. We also won numerous awards from the community for our service and that's all that mattered.

A few days after the *Hands Across America* event, I watched the evening news on television. I was shocked to hear a News Commentator said, "It hurts me to explain how some of the celebrities went to deliver some of the food that was purchased through the *Hands Across America* project. Thousands of dollars of food sat on the docks and were never delivered. This type of thing continued to happen in countries like Africa due to politics and wars." I felt repulsed after all the hard work and effort put forth as we organized hundreds of thousands to raise millions of dollars for the hungry and homeless. I guess Walker was right. When we tried to help people, corruption on man's part still hindered our good intentions.

I started to recall what Walker explained about the model prayer at Matthew 6:9-10. My mother had taught me to say this prayer as a child which stated, "Our Father which art in heaven. Hollowed be thy name. Thy kingdom come, Thy will be done, On earth as it is in heaven." (*The New Testament of Our Lord and Savior Jesus Christ, Revised Standard Version)* Walker helped me to see how I was praying that the same kind of conditions that exist in heaven, I wanted to see exist on earth. An earth without homeless or hungry people. Where sickness and death did not exist as well. Only Jehovah God through the rulership of his son Jesus Christ could touch the hearts of people to accomplish his will to eliminate problems throughout the earth.

Walker never made me feel stupid, but he would always lovingly show me answers to life's questions based on what the Bible said. I started to better understand what that prayer meant that I repeated over and over as a child and now as an adult. The imperfections of humans would always cause wars and conflicts. Any efforts of goodness could be thwarted by those that the devil can utilize to destroy good seeds of truth through lies and deceit. Only Jesus Christ who received power through God's holy spirit could battle this wicked spirit creature and defeat him and his demons. Jesus proved this as Michael the archangel when he cleansed heaven of these demonic forces as Revelation 12:7-9 reveals, "And there was war in heaven: Michael and his angels fought against the dragon; and the dragon fought and his angels, and prevailed not; neither was their place found anymore in heaven. And the great dragon was cast out, that old serpent, called the

Devil and Satan, which deceiveth the whole world: he was cast out into the earth, and his angels were cast out with him." (*King James Version*) God's powerful King Jesus Christ will also cleanse the earth in the future of Satan and his demons. We will then have peace and security without problems in the world as we see today.

I wished I had listened to what Walker had shown me in the Bible before I served as coordinator for *Hands Across America*. Days after the event, I discovered through news stories that most of the money from this fundraiser did not go to charities for the hungry and homeless. In certain countries, food rotted on docks due to war and government officials within that area. I was disappointed because of my hard work and faith in what the original purpose represented. My staff from Spotlight Productions had worked so hard as well. I was also three and a half months pregnant and very emotional. Walker was there to support me physically and spiritually. I still regularly attended Bethany Baptist church during this time. The pastor and I had become not just friends, but he was like a father to me. I wanted him to perform my wedding ceremony to Walker. We both agreed about our very special day.

Chapter 13

The Happiest Day of Our Lives: Our Wedding Day

It was June 7, 1986, our wedding day. I eagerly awaited this special day to marry Walker because I was not only pregnant with his child, but I loved this man. He developed into the type of man that would be a great husband and father. I appreciated the role Walker said he wanted to serve as head of our household. He based it on the way Jesus served as head of the Christian congregation with tenderness and love. Walker shared two scriptures that helped me see how even Jesus has a loving head and that is God at John 14:28 "YOU heard that I said to YOU, I am going away, and I am coming [back] to YOU. If YOU loved me, YOU would rejoice that I am going my way to the Father, because the Father is greater than I am." I appreciated the scripture also at 1 Peter 5:3, "not as domineering over those in your charge but being examples to the flock." (*Revised Standard Version)*

Our wedding day was Saturday, June 7, 1986. It was the happiest day of my life. I woke up with morning sickness because I was four months pregnant at the time with our first child. I purchased a reasonably priced wedding gown that gave me and the baby room to move about. The infant in my womb became quite busy especially at night. I watched as her little arms and feet stretched out across my stomach. Walker and I were amazed at the beautiful creation we had made together, thanks to God.

Our wedding ceremony was supposed to start at 4:00 p.m. By 3:00 p.m., I rushed to get my makeup done by my talented niece, Button. I wasn't a person for makeup, but I trusted my niece to do a good job, and Button did. After my makeup was completed, I carefully slipped into my white Chantilly laced gown. Yes, I wore white, although four months pregnant. This was my day and tradition, personal opinions of others had no place. I wore a crown covered with white flowers. My white veil had sprinkles of pearls throughout which came down to my waist and back. I finally felt beautiful.

I stayed at Janie's house overnight. She was my oldest sister who served in the place of my mother Elease who was now deceased. Mom had lived a difficult life. She gave birth to 14 children. Ten are still alive today. Our brother Joseph died as an infant. My oldest brother, Woodrow, is now deceased. An older sister named Trina, that many felt was the most beautiful young woman, got married, had two daughters Sharon and Joyce. She later died during childbirth. Elease was somewhat of a child herself when she got married. My mom started having children around the age of 13. Our father died when my twin sister and I were two years old. Elease had one-year- old twin boys as well at the time of my father's death. My other older siblings Janie, Deloris, Earlene, Linda, Edward, and Earlie or Buddy now deceased as well, took care of the younger five which consisted of Doris, my twin sister Bernadette as well as our twin brothers Wardell, Wendell, and me. My mother worked as a maid in the homes of white people to provide for us. We were a loving family that worked hard and took care of each other. I admired that about my mother. She raised some very decent individuals regardless of her many deficiencies. Elease did the best she could under the circumstances.

I was determined not to have children at such a young age. I wanted to enjoy my life and I did. At the age of 30, it was time for me to endeavor into a new life as a wife and mother with the man I loved.

I arrived at the Hilton Hotel in Claymont, Delaware around 3:45 p.m. I stayed upstairs in our bridal suite until it was time for our ceremony to start. I was extremely nervous. The time had arrived. My oldest brother Woodrow took my arm. My nieces Chante and Katrina served as my flower girls. They wore beautiful little white gowns covered with lace and ribbons. Walker's nephew little David served as my ring-bearer. My six bridesmaids marched in before me which consisted of my sisters Linda and Doris. My nieces Carol and Zenda followed. Walker's only sister Ocie served as a bridesmaid as well. Bernadette served as my maid-of-honor. Each bridesmaid wore stunning aqua colored gowns with white hats that matched. The groomsmen consisted of Walker's brothers Bobby, Steve, Sam, David and Walker's friends Gibson and another friend named Andre. Each groomsman wore black tuxedoes with white shirts. The adorable ring-bearer wore a black tuxedo as well. Janie my oldest sister, who served in the role of my deceased mother, wore a beautiful pink gown with a flattering pink hat. Both Walker and I were so proud of our family's loving support on that special wedding day.

Suddenly, the doors opened to the room where my ceremony was held. Walker and I decided to hold our wedding in a smaller banquet room. It was next to the Hilton's major banquet room where we held our reception. I walked slowly as Jerry Blake who dated my twin sister at the time, played our favorite song. He performed with the world renown R&B group *The Manhattans.* Jerry was tremendously talented. He played the jazzy version of Stevie Wonder's *Ribbons in the Sky.* I held my brother's arm tightly because I was nervous. Once I caught sight of Walker, I felt at ease as he smiled. I wanted to run down the aisle toward him. I no longer felt apprehensive about my life and who I would spend it with. It was Walker, the man I loved from the first time I saw him. Walker later revealed that he felt the same way when he saw me for the first time. Almighty God looked down from heaven, sprinkled our hearts so that Walker and I would become as one, in service to him forever.

I arrived and stood before God, Pastor Scott, and Walker. We looked intently into each other's eyes. We both smiled as our guests took their seats. Pastor Scott started the service as he asked, "Who give this woman to this man?" My oldest brother Woodrow responded, "I do." He smiled and removed my arm from his, gave me a hug and took a seat with the rest of my family. I appreciated how Woodrow was there for me in that role as my fatherly image now that my father Earlie was deceased.

Walker mentioned how he laughed to himself when just the night before at his bachelor's party, his oldest brother Bobby said, "I don't know how you got her to marry you." Bobby didn't see the man that I saw. I knew Walker would make a wonderful spiritual head, loving husband, father, brother, and friend.

Our cameraman David Brown for Spotlight Productions videotaped our wedding. We also had someone with a camera that shot photos. Lights flashed from the cameras, but I kept my eyes on Walker as Pastor Scott continued with the ceremony. I could see his eyes were filled with tears. I beamed as the pastor asked, "Claudette, do you take this man Walker Lee Carter to be your lawfully wedded husband? To have and to hold from this day forward. For better or for worse. For richer or for poorer. In sickness and in health. Till death do you part?" I was overexcited by now as I screamed, "I do." I had no clue that I would have to live up to every word I agreed to do before God on our wedding day. In our marriage, we experienced financial difficulties, sickness and eventually, Walker's death. I lived every word of my wedding vows during those thirty some years. He sat a beautiful example as he applied and fulfilled his vows before God up until his death.

The cameraman had now moved to an angle of a shot over the pastor's shoulder. I became a little annoyed, but we kept our eyes focused on each other. Pastor Scott looked sternly at Walker and then asked, "Walker, do you take this woman Claudette Dewanna Coleman to be your lawfully wedded wife? To have and to hold from this day forward. For better or for worse. For richer or poorer. In sickness and in health. Till death do you part?" Walker anxiously responded with a boyish grin, "I do." I could not help as I responded with girlish laughter.

Once our wedding vows were completed, Walker and I exchanged our rings. We had picked a beautiful zirconia ring priced at $19.00 for me. Yes. It wasn't a real diamond because that was all we could afford. I was so proud of that ring. It brought us together as husband and wife. Walker's ring was also less than $100. We were simply thrilled to be married to each other. Pastor Scott took both of our hands as he placed his on top and prayed. We humbly bowed our heads in honor of our loving God for this union. Immediately after the prayer, Pastor Scott proudly said in a loud voice, "I now pronounce you husband and wife. Walker you may kiss your bride." I don't remember Pastor Scott asking if there were any objections that they, "Should speak now or forever hold their peace." I believed with all my heart, that God, his son Jesus Christ and the myriads of angels lovingly approved of our marriage. My eyes radiated with blessedness as he kissed me lovingly. Our kiss lingered a few seconds as I inhaled the sweetness of his breath. I was finally Walker's wife and believed it would be forever.

We turned toward our guests as Pastor Scott said, "I present to you for the first time Mr. and Mrs. Walker and Claudette Carter." We slowly took each other's hands as entranced smiles consumed our faces. Walker and I walked insouciantly down the aisle as family and friends applauded exuberantly.

Excitement filled our hearts as we took photos that Walker and I cherished for the rest of our marriage together. We remained at the hotel within a courtyard to take our wedding photos. I started to feel overly excited due to the anticipation of our wedding reception. Walker and I arrived at the ballroom as we stood outside with our bridal party. The bridesmaids and the groomsmen took each other's arms as they awaited an introduction by my sister-in-law Marie who served as wedding coordinator.

The doors to the ballroom opened as each couple was introduced. Applauds filled the room. We would enter after Chante, Katrina and little David who served as my adorable flower girls and ringbearer. I fondly remembered how Marie announced our entrance into the ballroom. "And now for their first public appearance, I introduce the happy couple, Mr. and Mrs. Walker Lee Carter." I was thrilled as I heard those words. I did not care that my name was not mentioned because I wanted to be as one with Walker. The reception was filled with thunderous applause, screams, and whistles.

Marie directed us to the dance floor. It was time for our first dance as husband and wife. Once again, our favorite song was played which was *Ribbons in the Sky* by Stevie Wonder. Walker was such a smooth dancer. We had gained quite a reputation for a particular dance that he taught me. Walker pulled me close. My petite stature with a four-month, pregnant belly did not deter us. The three of us which included our child within my womb were jubilant. I could feel my child's blissful movement as if she approved. He bent down and whispered in my ear, "I am so happy. I love you baby." I looked up at Walker and uttered softly, "I love you too." Our family and guests clapped but we were elevated in our love for each other. We gazed into each other's eyes. It was that very moment I saw true love and I knew Walker's God; Jehovah had sent me this man. I was determined to comprehend more about his God. The song slowly concluded. I felt we had returned from a heavenly place.

I started to feel a little light-headed. Earlier, I tasted a few of the appetizers but now it was dinner time. We had the normal chicken dinner which was delectable. I wanted my family and guests to enjoy our wedding reception and the food as well. It was obvious they did. Glasses started to cling. I had no idea that it meant Walker and I was supposed to kiss. We finally did. A few minutes later Bobby, Walker's oldest brother, got up to make a speech. His mom and dad were Jehovah's Witnesses, and a toast was inappropriate. He respected that and just said, "Yes. I did tell my brother Walker that he could not get or deal with a woman like Claudette because she had too much going for herself. I was wrong because they seem so happy together. So, I wish them the very best. Congratulations you two."

Bernadette then stood up. Drew a sigh of relief and stated, "Yes. I agree with Bobby that this match of my sister and Walker would never work but we will see. They have been in love since high school, so finally today, they became husband and wife. I am so happy for them and may God bless this union. Congratulations Walker and Claudette." Finally, I received Bernadette's public approval before all our family. She never wanted to go against the family's opinion as well as her own regarding Jehovah's Witnesses or me marrying one.

After dinner, dancing, and the speeches, we mingled with our family and guests. A distinguished variety of people from all races and backgrounds attended. Co-workers who became dear friends from Upper Merion Township. Robert Wright, who is now a Delaware County Judge and his beautiful wife Florence who is also an attorney. A host of other lawyers that I worked with. Supervisors and executives from American Cablevision, now known as Comcast. Bill Manlove, Bob Young, and other coaches and their wives attended from Widener University. Walker's best friend Jonathan Holland better known as Spike and his funny wife Shereese who shared so many happy memories with us attended as well. Walker and I were so thankful for our families, friends, and guests that surrounded us with love and support on our very special wedding day. We had completed our dream wedding, now it was time to deal with reality.

After our wedding, Walker and I moved back to 503 Parker Street in Chester, which was my brother Edward and his wife Tina's home. We moved there with my family when we came from the south. The rent was reasonable because I had left my job in Upper Merion. I felt like we were going backwards because of good and bad memories in this home now that my mother had died, and Edward and Tina had moved on as well. It was what we could afford with only Walker's income. I felt weird that we returned to a home with so much of my past that now fulfilled my future.

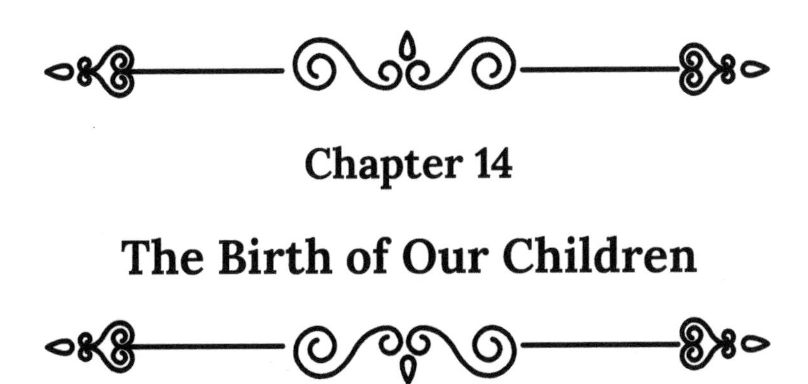

Chapter 14

The Birth of Our Children

Five months after our wedding about midnight on November 11, 1986, my water broke. Walker rushed me to Crozer Hospital in Chester. Our first daughter challenged me with seventeen hours of labor before she came into the world. I was exhausted from the pain although I had received an epidural that caused only my right leg to go limp. Seventeen hours later, which felt like an eternity, Doctor McCray delivered our daughter, Wanisha Suzzette Carter. Her faint little cry assured us that Wanisha had breath of life. I held her on my chest practically breathless as the nurses cleaned her up. The intensity of love for this little creature infused me with strength. She looked at me with a feeling of tranquility as the nurses wrapped our newborn in a blanket and handed this blessing to Walker. He immediately replied as tears rolled down his face, "Thank you Jehovah for this beautiful gift you have given Claudette and me. She will serve you all the days of her life. That I promise Heavenly Father in the name of your dear son Jesus Christ I ask this for Wanisha. Amen." One of the nurses commented, "Wow! What a beautiful prayer. You're going to make a wonderful father." I started to cry because it was as if Walker knew this was a precious gift from Jehovah and he pledged that our child would serve him.

I found enough strength, raised my right hand to wipe away his tears. Walker leaned over and kissed me. I felt a sense of peace. I drifted off into a deep sleep for hours. Later that evening on the 12th, we had a steak and lobster dinner which was a gift from the hospital for new parents. The following day, Walker and I, along with our new baby, returned to our home on Parker Street. Some residents called the area little Vietnam because it was near the William Penn projects where people were shot, drugs were sold, and violence was abundant. We prayed a lot. I started to study the Bible more with my mother-in-law Susie and father-in-law Walker. I desperately wanted all Almighty God's protection while we lived in that area. I would often be at home alone with our new baby at night while Walker worked double shifts to take care of our family. These were difficult times, but we survived.

Three months after the birth of my first child, I was pregnant again with our second child. I was frustrated with myself on how I could allow this to happen. When I told Walker, he was thrilled and expressed, "Now, Wanisha will have a sister or brother to grow up with. We both came from big families, so everything will be alright with Jehovah's help." He held me in his arms, and I believed that everything would be just fine. Nine months later, our daughter Jaleesa Elease Carter arrived. We decided to make our second daughter's middle name Elease in honor of my mother. Once again, in the delivery room, Walker took Jaleesa in his arms and said to her, "You are a gift from Jehovah, and Jaleesa, you will serve him as well. In the name of your precious son Jesus Christ, I ask this for my daughter Jaleesa. Amen." An air of peacefulness filled the room as our new baby girl looked arduously into her father's eyes. There was just an immediate bond between Walker and this child as he held our baby. When he returned Jaleesa to my arms, I sensed Jehovah had brought our family together. I believed all four of us would serve him forever. I was drawn ever closer to Walker's God Jehovah.

People would often comment what good babies both Wanisha and Jaleesa were. They were not babies who cried a lot or up at nights. I eventually went back to work as a secretary for Chester Township. I continued to run Spotlight Productions as its Executive Director. I would come home from work at 5:00 p.m., make sure my daughters and Walker had their dinner so that the girls would be in bed by 8:30 p.m. They were only a year apart at one and two years old. Yet, they would sleep throughout the nights. I was blessed with as people would call them, "good babies." People asked me what my secret was? I would try to come up with reasons. I knew one of the secrets was that I played cassette tapes of publications like *My Book of Bible Stories* published by Watch Tower Bible and Tract Society of Pennsylvania while both of our daughters were in my womb. Even when their little feet or arms stretched across my belly, I would play these Bible stories and it calmed them down. I sensed that they listened to what God tried to teach them while in my womb. It drew me closer to this God Jehovah and his son Jesus Christ. I was determined to know more about them through my study of the Bible.

I understood my family and friends would not approve. We were raised as Baptist to believe what we were taught in church. I found it to be limited and did not answer questions such as, what really happens when you die and why do people of the same religion such as Baptists, Catholics, or Orthodox go to war against each other even today? If their religion is based on the teachings of Jesus Christ, shouldn't they love one another? Walker was not a baptized servant of Jehovah. I didn't care anymore. I wanted to discover what Jehovah's Witnesses were about for myself. It was not about the religion but my personal relationship with the true God and his son Jesus Christ.

While I studied the Bible more, I could see Walker's love for his job at PECO Energy increased. He had been trained well by one of his friends through lineman school. Walker often talked about lighting on the streets and even those generator areas that were fenced in. It was strange that certain lights on the streets would go out whenever we passed and then come back on once we passed in our vehicle. He seemed to have a certain passion or connection with electricity. I often dismissed it as just something strange or unusual.

I loved the relationship Walker had with our daughters. When he came home from work and our girls were about two and three years old, there was total excitement that daddy was home. Wanisha and Jaleesa ran toward the door as soon as it opened and screamed, "Mommy, daddy is home. We missed you." I felt our life was like a dream. It was the epitome of what I dreamed my life would be like. Smiles consumed his face as he lifted both girls up in his arms.

One particular day, I read a story to our daughters earlier. They showed the book to Walker and started to ask questions about this fairytale book called *Sleeping Beauty*. Wanisha showed Walker the book that was given to them by a neighbor. She said, "It was scary daddy." He sat down on the sofa in the living room with Wanisha on his left and Jaleesa on his right. I sat down in a chair nearby as Walker asked, "Did anything bad happen in this book when mommy read it to you?" Wanisha answered with excitement, "The witch put a spell on Sleeping Beauty and that's why she couldn't wake up." He then asked, "Would you want someone to do that to you or your sister?" Wanisha answered, "No. That witch was very bad." Jaleesa agreed, "She was bad." Walker asked, "Then how do you think Jehovah and Jesus feel about us reading what bad people do to hurt other people?" Wanisha said, "Jehovah or Jesus would not like that. It's like magic." Jaleesa shook her head and replied, "No. He don't like that."

I watched as Walker got up slowly and said to our daughters, "Wait there, I want you to hear how Jehovah feels about things like magic and spells being put on people. He grabbed a large reference Bible. Walker turned to a scripture in Leviticus 19:31 and read, "Do not turn yourselves to the spirit mediums, and do not consult professional foretellers of events, so as to become unclean by them. I am Jehovah your God." He then explained what a spirit medium and foreteller of events was in simple terms that the girls could understand. Wanisha replied, "They're like witches and they're bad." Jaleesa agreed, "Witches are bad." Without hesitation Wanisha asked, "Can we throw this bad book away?" Walker replied, "No problem baby girls." He hugged both girls. I came over and apologized, "I'm sorry girls. Mommy didn't think about how Jehovah would not like us reading about magic and spells. We must thank Jehovah and daddy for teaching us something very good. Walker defended me immediately, "Jehovah knows mommy didn't know that. He understands and still loves all of us." We hugged each other as I thought, "I loved how Walker took on his role as head of our household. We were truly happy. But I knew the questions by our daughters would not end there."

I loved the prayers Walker shared with the girls and me at dinner time. He poured his heart out for his family as if Walker stood before Jehovah's throne in heaven. His faith was strong but still Walker had made no attempt to become a baptized servant of Jehovah. Finally, when Jaleesa was three years old, she asked her dad, "Who is Jehovah?" He hesitated momentarily and explained, "Baby girl, Jehovah is our Creator. He made us. Without Jehovah we wouldn't be here. He put you in mommy's tummy. He loves us so much and then Jehovah teaches us to love him, his son Jesus Christ and each other." Wanisha, now four years old immediately responded, "I love Jehovah. I love you daddy, mommy, my sister, and the whole world." Walker laughed and said, "That's wonderful Wanisha. I love you too baby girl."

It was these expressions of love that drew our family closer together. Walker loved giving simple Bible explanations and illustrations to our daughters. He could see they needed more explanations from the both of us as their parents. It was vital that I continued my Bible study so that I could help our daughters as well. Walker continued to try to help Jaleesa understand God's name as he explained, "The word God is a title like I call you baby girl. But your mom and I gave you a name which is Jaleesa. So, God has a name, and it is Jehovah." She smiled with two front teeth missing and said, "I understand daddy. God needs to have a name like we all do." I was proud and thankful that he took the role as head of our family and teacher of God's word. I was mesmerized by Walker's expression of love for God and other people in general. Yes, Walker had many imperfections just like I had. Within him, Walker became an amazing father, husband, brother, and friend. He had received numerous awards and accolades in football, track, and life. Yet he remained humble and loving. I was really in love with this man, and I trusted him. I believed God had made this man for me. Yes. What a man! Each of us smiled with a source of comfort which could have only come from Jehovah.

Walker worked for PECO Energy, a subsidiary of Exelon as a full time First-Class Lineman. He continued to work part-time at Widener University as its first black assistant coach for football and track. Walker had won numerous awards in track and field as an athlete at Widener. It was inevitable that he would become a great coach because Walker had dedicated his life to the university. Bob Young served as head coach for Widener's Track team. The year I graduated from Widener in 1985, our yearbook described the track team's accomplishments as, "*Year of the All-American*." The article described how "Widener has enjoyed a rich tradition in athletics over the years, and the leading sport for individual achievement, especially as far as All-American status is concerned, is men's track."

Under the coaching of Bob Young and Walker, "Widener won the M.A.C. indoor title and placed third in the outdoor conference championship. In the process, Widener came away with its 14th All- American in the indoor nationals Jim Wardle, a triple jumper, also javelin thrower, Bill Miller, became Widener's 15th All-American in the outdoor championships. Widener also had two other qualifiers for outdoor nationals including long jumper, Jeff Williams, and hurdler, Todd Patterson. Jim Brittain, a standout discus thrower, almost qualified for the trip to the nationals." The women's track team for Widener was also rejuvenated under the training of Bob as head coach and Walker as assistant coach.

When our daughters Wanisha and Jaleesa were about five and six years old, I enjoyed going to Schwartz Athletic Center on Widener's campus. They watched Bob and Walker coach indoor track to the students. After practice was over, he allowed our daughters to run around the track a few times as he coached them. I watched from the sidelines with a source of pride. I was delighted to see how he enjoyed spending time with our daughters. Walker had evolved into an amazing husband and father.

In the springtime, I would also take our daughters to Coach Young and Walker's men and women's outdoor track and field. Practice was held at the Leslie C. Quick Jr. Stadium. Wanisha and Jaleesa loved this new stadium that was opened in 1994. They were about seven and eight years old at that time. It fascinated the girls to be able to run around this new track with their dad. I sat on the bleachers as they jumped into Walker's arms at the finish line of their pretend track meet.

Walker and I also loved the annual football banquets for the players, coaches, and their wives. The Pioneers under the tutelage of Bill Manlove and his coaching staff established a reputation as national champions throughout Philadelphia and Delaware County areas. On widenerpride.com, an article described their winning history this way, "Teamwork is essential to achieving victory in any sport. For Widener University's football program, it has racked up 715 victories in its 140 seasons of football. Included in that total are the 13 wins it put together to win the NCAA Division III championship in 1981 for the second national title in school history."

In both national championships, Walker was a stand-out performer either as a player or coach. I enjoyed those banquets because he worked hard as an athlete and coach for Widener. He beamed whenever we attended these special events. We were treated with respect as the only black couple at the coaches and their wives' tables. Walker had such compassion, love, and appreciation for people of all races. He lovingly taught me based on my teachings from the Bible that I should walk in the footsteps of Jesus Christ because he felt the same way.

I remembered how Walker talked about the coaching staff for Widener under Bill, "I have tremendous love and respect for these men and their families. We have won National Championships and National Semifinals. They know and love the game of football and so do I. They do not care that I am a black man but that I was a man who loved the game." I was compelled to support Walker in whatever he pursued. He taught me based on the Bible not to judge people by their skin color. I admired the woman I became with Walker as a wife, mother, sister, and friend.

It was important that I supported Walker more in his part-time position as assistant coach. I invited my cameraman David Brown from Spotlight Productions. I interviewed coach Young and Walker for their major accomplishments with the men and women's track and field teams. We filmed both as they coached their student-athletes. I started my interview with Walker. "Hello, I am Claudette Carter, your host of *Delaware Valley Spotlight*. I'm here with Walker Carter, my husband who is the first black assistant coach in football, and track for Widener University." I was nervous but determined to enlighten others about who this man was and what Walker had accomplished at the university. I then asked, "How do you feel about the work you are doing here at Widener?" Walker smiled and responded, "I appreciate this opportunity to coach such talented young men and women here at Widener. Such outstanding athletes in the 4x100 relay teams like Ron Hodge, Gary Foster, and Gibson Ivery, who still holds the Widener Track and Field record of 41.29."

I was convinced that due to his humility, Walker would not acknowledge any of his achievements. I decided to ask, "You were also a part of that historical 4x100 record-setting relay team, right? He vacillated for a few moments and then stated, "Yes. I was." I knew I wanted to convey more of his accomplishments, so I explained, "In 1976 and 1977 you were named an NCAA All-American in Track & Field as member of the 4x100 relay teams. He smiled and said, "You did your research. Very nice." I appreciated Walker's humility. I continued to explain, "With all those accomplishments you can see why you were appointed as assistant coach for track and field. We laughed as Walker asked, "Do you have any more questions for me, or do you just want to promote me as your husband?" "Well, I will be back to interview you during the football season where one reporter stated, "Walker Carter was a stand-out performer for the Pioneer football team that won the MAC championship in 1975 and 1977—making a semi-final run in the NCAA Playoffs in 1975 and then achieving Widener's first NCAA Division III Football National Championship in 1977." I could tell he started to feel uneasy, "Well, I will see how I feel about your interview then because remember all of these achievements takes team effort." I agreed and thanked Walker for his interview.

I also interviewed head coach Bob Young. He was a man that was strong in his Christian faith. His wife Jackie was one of the most genuine women I had ever met. Bob and Jackie were just a very sweet and loving couple. During the interview, coach Young excitedly expressed, "Our Men's Indoor Track and Field team has won numerous Middle Atlantic Conferences and we will continue to be victorious because of the talented young people here at Widener. We also won the Men's Outdoor Track and Field Middle Atlantic Conference starting from 1965 and practically every year since. Outstanding performers such as Billy Whiteshoes Johnson, Walker and so many more have been a part of that history. We have won more than 40 awards." I immediately responded, "Wow! That's outstanding. First, I would like to thank both you and Walker for your responses and taking the time for these interviews." Coach Young thanked me as I turned toward the television camera and said, "This is Claudette Carter here at Widener University for *Delaware Valley Spotlight."*

Our cable television production company had accomplished tremendous work within the community. We won numerous awards for *Outstanding Community Programming* from American Cable and community service awards from the NAACP. Wherever there was news to report, Spotlight tried to be there. We televised top entertainers on *Delaware Valley Spotlight.* I continued to work a part-time schedule after I married Walker and our daughters were born.

Now that I had a family of my own that I was proud of, I wanted my husband and our daughters Wanisha and Jaleesa to visit my hometown of Mullins, South Carolina. When our daughters were about four and five years old, we took them to Disney in

Florida. On our way, we spent the night at a hotel in my hometown, Mullins, South Carolina so that Walker and our daughters could see the origin of the Coleman family. I was proud of my hometown. We rode throughout Mullins as I introduced my husband and children to a host of cousins like Carolyn, Bruce, Denise, and Earl. All my father's brothers and sisters had moved up north or were deceased. My mother's two brothers were also deceased. We enjoyed visiting their children such as my cousin's brother, who moved from New York and returned to Mullins to become the well-known Judge Graves. We would stay with him and his wife Jackie on our way to Myrtle Beach or Florida. Walker loved to visit my hometown and could find his way around Mullins better than I could. I enjoyed showing my husband and our children the tobacco and cotton fields that surrounded Mullins. I explained how and why my brothers and sisters had to work long days in those fields for our family's survival. We enjoyed our visits to Mullins as a family. When we returned home in Chester, we would go back to our family's routines of work and raising our daughters.

Once or twice a week, I would have my Bible study lessons with Walker's mom and dad. By 1991, I left the church and became a baptized Jehovah's Witness. Pastor Scott, who married us, had passed and I just didn't feel like I belonged there anymore. I discovered so many scriptures in the Bible that taught me about Jehovah and his son Jesus Christ. I was taught previously that they were a trinity. Now I could see based on such scriptures as John 17:3, Hebrews 12:2 or Philippians 2:9-11 which explained, "Wherefore God also hath highly exalted him, and given him a name which is above every name: That at the name of Jesus every knee should bow, of things in heaven, and things in earth, and things under the earth. And that every tongue should confess that Jesus Christ is Lord, to the glory of God the Father." This was quoted from my *King James Version.* I prayed to God fervently, "Please whoever you are, I want to know your name so that I can call on you. I need to know because I don't want to just serve any god but the true God." Eventually my prayer was answered. I now could see in the scriptures that God had a name and at Psalms 83:18 in my version, "That men may know that thou, whose name alone is JE-HO VAH, art the most high over all the earth." Finally, I could call God by his name as I asked for answers to my prayers in Jesus' name. This was a revelation for me.

I was thrilled to learn also what the model prayer that Jesus taught us to pray meant to me. Based on Matthew 6:10, I was taught by my mother to say, "Thy kingdom come. Thy will be done in earth, as it is in heaven." I made sure that I read scriptures from my Bible, *The Holy Bible Old and New Testaments in the King James Version.* I was told by family and friends that, "Jehovah's Witnesses were a cult, and they have their own Bible." I was determined to use my King James version on every Bible study, although the language was hard to understand at times. I repeated every night as a child this model prayer but never fully understood its purpose. During my study and after numerous prayers, I started to understand how Jehovah God placed Jesus as ruler and King, over this kingdom. This kingdom would rid the earth of all its problems such as sickness, death, pain, sorrow, and war. This was the solution I had been looking for.

Chapter 15

We Moved from Chester into Our New Home

Walker and I, as well as our daughters, remembered the true stories by my mother-in-law Susie about the land we would build our new home on. She was born and raised outside of Chester in Media, Pennsylvania. Susie was born during a time when the city of Chester was inhabited by white families. Black families or slaves that fled from the south lived on the outskirts of Chester. Today, these areas outside of Chester are considered as the suburbs filled with expensive real estate.

I appreciated that my mother-in-law and father-in-law had such rich historical backgrounds. My father-in-law Walker Wesley Carter lived about a mile from Susie. The area where they were raised in Media, and Lima, Pennsylvania inspired the Oscar-nominated film *Seabiscuit* starring Tobey Maguire and Jeff Bridges. Streets are named in the development near us such as Secretariat and War Admiral. Wolff's Apple House is also a prominent source within our community. Susie played and picked apples in the fields of Wolff's orchard as a young girl. She also walked to the first Wawa store for milk which was established in 1964. Walker's family has a rich source of history in the surrounding areas.

There are things within our community that inspired a proud source of history for my mother-in-law Susie. There was also some tragic history that was also included within this area. Years after I was married to Walker, I discovered the horrifying experience of Susie's brother Alexander McClay Williams. At the age of 16, he was sent to a juvenile institution after starting a barn fire. Alexander was somewhat mentally challenged. He was falsely accused of killing a white female staff member named Vida Robare who worked at the institution. Alexander was unfortunately found guilty by an all-white male jury and put to death by electrocution. When they electrocuted him, a telephone book was placed underneath Alexander's 125-pound body which was so diminutive due to his small stature. My mother-in-law described how Alexander never fully comprehended why he was being put to death. Tears rolled down his face. Suddenly, more than 2,000 volts of electricity pummeled the body of Alexander on June 8th, 1931. Years later, he was acquitted for this crime. Susie and our family were still devastated years later by this source of injustice. In 2017, more than 86 years later, Attorney Robert Keller represented Alexander, pro bono to prove his innocence. Ocie Williams the daughter of Susie sent a message that explained, "The DA has agreed to grant a partial expunge of Uncle Alex's record. Meaning the verdict is removed but the court docket number and record/file will remain as the record." My mother-in-law responded, "I wanted my brother Alexander's record completely cleared."

It was later discovered during an interview on *Fox 29 News,* that the murdered woman was killed by her husband Fred. It was a crime of passion. The victim was stabbed more than 47 times. Fred's great-niece Teresa Smithers stated, "My ancestor got away with murder." Chris O'Connell, a reporter with *Fox,* spoke with Teresa over the telephone: "She told us that her uncle came from a very abusive and alcoholic family and after doing her own research, she even believes Alexander McClay Williams was framed." During his report, O'Connell explained, "In a stunning revelation not known until recently, they learned Vida Robare had divorced her husband nine years earlier in Michigan. The reason she stated in the records, 'Extreme cruelty.' The belief is that Robare killed his wife in a fit of rage and framed it on the closest delinquent he could find and don't take their word for it."

News reporter O'Connell mentioned during the broadcast how Sam Lemon, an outstanding author, was interviewed during the *Fox 29 News* interview. "Lemon has been researching this case for the past 30 years because his great-grandfather, William Ridley, was the attorney who originally represented Williams during his murder trial." With tremendous compassion, Lemon expressed, "The image of him sitting in that electric chair with a hood over his head, I can't get that out of my mind. This story haunts me."

Our family agreed with Sam. This experience with Alexander's electrocution and later found innocent is still visitant to our family today. It was heart wrenching for me when Walker was tragically electrocuted on his job. These deplorable tribulations where an uncle and nephew were both electrocuted is not only tragic but still resurges horrifying memories. It is my continuous study of the Bible that cultivates the hope of the resurrection based on Acts 24: 15 which guarantees, "And I have hope toward God, which hope these men also look forward to, that there is going to be a resurrection of both the righteous and the unrighteous." *(New World Translation of the Holy Scriptures)* This tremendous hope from God's word sustains me. I know for a fact that I will see both Walker, Uncle Alexander, and numerous other family members and friends who are deceased. I will see them again because Jehovah God through his son Jesus Christ promises, "and is based on a hope of the everlasting life that God, who cannot lie, promised long ago;" Titus 1:2. *(NWT)*

Our move from Chester was a blessing from God. Both of our daughters Wanisha and Jaleesa were in grade school at the time. Chester's school system had changed for the worst. The Rose Tree Media school district was one of the best in the country where my in-laws lived. The house was an old family home where my Susie had grown up. Walker and I planned to build a house with in-law quarters for his parents. We were swindled out of a down payment for a log home that my husband wanted. So that idea fell through. The land was also so-called surveyed with the pretense that it folded over into itself or that half of our land was under our neighbor's home. We knew this was possibly untrue. My mother-in-law's family reside near each other years ago in about four different homes on acres of this land. That may have caused the confusion. Now the land became less than an acre. The house we had planned to build with in-law quarters was too large. Walker's parents decided to let us buy the property. My in-laws moved back to Chester. Walker and I realized this area did consist of painful memories for his mother. She was born and raised on this land with her sisters and brothers. Susie wanted the property to stay within the family. Walker and I purchased the land and built our home.

Walker and I tore down the old house and built a new one so that our daughters would be in a better school district. Our family appreciated that so much. We now lived near Walker's aunts who were Susie's sisters. We spent many days at their homes for the *Sister's Luncheons.* It consisted of card games such as pinochle and some of the best food I had ever tasted. Tables would be filled with turkey and stuffing, collard greens, fresh baked rolls that were larger than a man's fist. Homemade mint iced tea. Meatloaf and mashed potatoes. For dessert, fresh baked apple pies. All of Walker's aunts were great cooks. My mother-in-law Susie named her daughter after her sister Ocie. Both talented women established reputations as the family's greatest cooks.

It was always a pleasure when we were invited to these luncheons either at Aunt Alice's or Aunt Beatrice's homes. Both grew up and resided in this same Media area. Mom's other sister Aunt Frances lived in Delaware at the time. We would go to her house for pinochle and delectable food quite often. Walker's family became like my family.

Not long after we moved into our newly constructed home in 1997, both of Walker's Aunts Alice and Beatrice had passed. Each of their homes were sold by their children to Caucasian buyers. The area started to change completely based on who could afford to live in this area as well as increase of taxes. Today, very few black families live in these where my in-laws resided and grew up as children. The high-priced real estate and taxes are some of the primary reasons.

My in-laws would often share cherished stories about the Media area they were born and raised in. Their family legacy continues to linger for our children to experience. Before the death of my father-in-law, Susie would share with our daughters how she met their grandfather. Photos would be displayed to show where they attended schools in Rose Tree Media school district along with their brothers and sisters. Eventually, they met as teenagers while my father-in-law played baseball. My mother-in-law Susie was also a well-known basketball player in the area. There was a rich source of family history in this area that would never be forgotten.

We were so happy with our new home. Walker would often come home from work excited about what he had accomplished for his family. Our daughters even put their handprints on the side of the cemented porch. I also wrote the words "praise Jah" as well. We felt our home was a blessing from our God Jehovah. The four of us danced often within our home due to the joy we felt.

A few years after Walker was employed with PECO, a company out of Chicago called Exelon merged with PECO Energy. He was hyper-excited. Walker danced and said, "I love Jehovah God, my family, friends, and my job. Today I got the opportunity to ride with the Vice President of the company. We both attended Widener and he is really a nice guy. His name is Mike Innocenzo. I had a great day thanks to Jehovah." He looked at me smiled and said, "Kid, you and the girls are the best thing that has happened to me. Thank you for marrying me so that God could give us this beautiful family." I thought to myself, "I have never seen Walker so elated and proud that everything seemed to be going well. All his dreams had been fulfilled as he continued to give God and his son Jesus Christ the glory for what he accomplished." I knew things would not remain in this happy state.

Chapter 16

Our 25th Wedding Celebration

On June 4, 2011, Walker and I celebrated our 25th wedding anniversary. We held this special event at the Hilton Hotel in Claymont, Delaware. Walker and I arrived after 3:00 p.m. to check in because we decided to stay overnight. Both of us were ecstatic to see what our daughters Wanisha and Jaleesa along with my best friend Debbie Mitchell had created for our 25 years of marriage. I purchased a beautiful pale blue gown with rhinestones throughout the top. Walker looked so handsome in his black tuxedo, light blue bowtie, light blue vest that matched my dress and a white shirt. I held Walker's hand as we arrived at the ballroom doors in the same location our wedding reception was held 25 years ago. The doors swung open as my heart pounded from excitement.

The banquet room was filled with many of the same people that attended our wedding 25 years ago. Well-dressed family and friends applauded as we entered the room. The women were dressed in gorgeous evening gowns and the men had a variety of handsome tuxedoes and suits. The ballroom was ravishing. White linen tablecloths with various colors of flowers and candelabras that emanated soft lighting in the room. There was a wonderfully decorated head table with aqua and white flowers. Fine porcelain and silverwares graced the tables with colorful napkins. Walker and I stood in the entrance as we admired the aesthetics of the ballroom. We continued to hold hands as our daughters came over, gave us a hug and escorted us to the head table. They sat with us as well. Tears of joy rolled down my face. We looked at one another and felt that we were blessed. I then looked at Wanisha and Jaleesa and cried, "It's so beautiful. I didn't expect all of this. Thanks so much." The applause ceased as Walker and I hugged both our daughters. We both turned toward Debbie who was seated at a table near us and thanked her as well.

Suddenly, our guests screamed, "Happy 25th anniversary!" Walker looked at me and said, "Happy anniversary baby. I hope and pray we'll be together, 25 or more years, with Jehovah's blessing." I slowly touched the left side of Walker's face. We smiled at each other. There was something about that very tender moment that his prayer would go unanswered. Both Walker and I had become baptized servants of Jehovah God as well as our daughters. We had become a family that served the highest God as we followed in the footsteps of his son Jesus Christ. We had it all. But did we? Unfortunately, as I looked away from Walker and considered how I just can't relinquish the thought that this would possibly be our last major anniversary celebration together. I started to think we would never make it to 50 years of marriage. I felt doleful about the possibility of losing him. I consoled myself so that I could return to reality. I reasoned, "True love just does not last in this crazy world." I shook my head, smiled as I looked at Walker and thought, "This is a wonderful celebration. I needed to get myself together so that I can enjoy this special evening."

Dinner was served at our table first. Our daughters had selected a delicious chicken dish with rice pilaf and mixed vegetables. While we ate dinner, I started to reminisce as we celebrated this 25th wedding anniversary. It reminded me of our God given arrangement of marriage from our Heavenly Father. I considered my marriage to be one of God's most spectacular gifts for Walker and me. We served Almighty God together as husband and wife. Now that our daughters were both in their mid-twenties, they made their decisions to serve Jehovah as they imitated Jesus Christ as our Lord and savior. They had become young, Christian women admired and loved by so many people. Our love for God and others, based on the teachings of the Bible had solidified us into a real family. We were truly thankful as our love abounded.

It was interesting to see that Walker was in a deep thought process during dinner as well. He later mentioned that during dinner, "I looked at you as my wife and our two daughters. A smile came across my face as our anniversary celebration continued. I felt a sense of pride as the best imperfect, human husband, and father. I introduced you to the true God and the true teachings in his word. I don't know if we will have another 25 years together as husband and wife. I do know that if one of us dies, we both have the hope of the resurrection just as Jesus promised. We will live together in paradise on earth forever with our daughters where sickness, death, pain, or sorrow will no longer exist. I feel good about our past and future." Those words Walker said seemed out of place, but I felt comforted.

Now that we had completed dinner, Walker grabbed my right hand. It was time for our first dance at our 25th anniversary celebration. He escorted me to the dance floor as all eyes watched us carefully. Most of our family and guests knew what a smooth dancer Walker was. I just followed as he rhythmically led me in creative dance movements. We looked affectionately into each other's eyes. Walker and I felt as if we were lifted within our own segment of love. The doors to the ballroom opened suddenly, as our song played. This was the song we danced off 25 years ago at our wedding. We stopped our dance for a few moments as Stevie Wonder entered the room. He sang *Ribbons in the Sky* magnificently. I screamed, "This can't be the real Stevie Wonder. Know y'all didn't bring one of my favorite artists here for our anniversary? Walker just laughed as he looked at me and said, "Baby, that's C.P. Lacey. That multi-talented entertainer and comedian." Once Lacey came closer, I saw that he pretended to be Stevie Wonder. "He was so convincing." We continued to dance as the music played and Lacey sang,

"Oh, so long for this night I prayed.
That a star would guide you my way
To share with me this special day
Where ribbons in the sky for our love..."

Walker and I were transferred to our wedding day 25 years ago. This was a special time for us, and we were captivated in our love for each other. We both hugged C.P. Lacey once he completed our favorite song. Walker shook his hand again and said, "You are really the greatest impersonator I have ever seen. You are talented. Wow! I almost believed you were Stevie Wonder. Thanks, man, for doing a great job on our song." I became emotional and said, "C.P. that meant so much to us. You are very talented. Thanks again." We returned to our table as our celebration continued.

Once we were seated, our oldest daughter Wanisha went to the podium to speak. She was elegantly dressed in a beautiful blue gown. With a tremendous source of maturity and grace Wanisha expressed to Walker and me, "Mom and Dad, please return to the dance floor as we prepare for the next source of entertainment." Walker once again took my hand and led me quickly to the dance floor. In a calm and loving voice, she said, "First of all I thank Jehovah for my parents. Jaleesa and I had the privilege to be raised in a home where our parents loved each other dearly for over 25 years and their love is still strong thanks to Jehovah. As your first born, I am proud to be your daughter. I love you both." We returned kisses in the air and screamed, "We love you too baby-girl." I selfishly thought to myself, "Yes. No matter how old our daughters are, they will always be our babies."

Amid some applause, our youngest daughter Jaleesa arrived at the podium. She was dressed in a stunning blue gown as well. In a voice of acquiescence with tears in her eyes Jaleesa said, "I thank Jehovah for you two. I love you and dad. Happy anniversary! Now, before I really start crying, can we have all the married couples, especially my grandparents join our mom and dad on the dance floor? This is our version of the Marriage Game. The music will start to play and as the number of years you have been married are mentioned, each couple will leave the dance floor at that time please." I admired how both of daughters had blossomed spiritually in their service and love for God. This empowered both of our daughters to become admirable young women. Walker looked at me as the music started and we began to dance and said, "I am so thankful for my family. This has been so nice." I could only smile and express, "I agree." We continued to dance as the numbers of years were mentioned, "One to five. Five to ten. Ten to fifteen. Fifteen to twenty. Twenty to twenty-five years and so-on. We graciously left the dance floor. Our number of years of marriage were completed. It was time to leave.

Very few couples remained as our daughters screamed, "Thirty to forty. Forty to fifty. Fifty to sixty." Walker's mother Susie and his dad Walker were the only couple that remained and now left the dance floor. They had been married almost 59 years. A chill penetrated my body as I thought how I appreciated what my in-laws had accomplished but I knew we would never reach that goal. Wanisha shouted, "Congratulations grampy! You and grandmom won." The crowd filled the ballroom with applause. They were a source of pride as both Walker and Susie had been married longer than any other couple in the room that night. I still wondered even at that time why his mom and dad did not name my husband Walker, Jr., rather than Walker Lee? I'm sure they had their reasons. It was time for me to refocus on the conclusion of a magnificent, 25th wedding anniversary celebration as it came to a conclusion.

When Walker and I returned to our room at the hotel, it was filled with gifts. We were so thankful to Jehovah for the genuine love we had received from family members, our spiritual brothers, and sisters as well as other friends. I remembered how we hugged each other and smiled as Walker attempted to dance with me once again. We were so happy. What a wonderful night this was for the celebration of our 25th wedding anniversary.

Chapter 17

The Wedding Day of Our Oldest Daughter

Wanisha, our oldest daughter, is a strong woman who loved and served Jehovah as well. She was a regular pioneer in the Christian congregation. Wanisha met Muhammad Bey, who was also a faithful servant of Jehovah through her spiritual sister and best friend Nisha, during the winter months of 2014. After a few months of dating, Walker and I got to know this young brother. We spent time in field service for hours during the week. Muhammad knew that we were protective of our daughter Wanisha, especially her dad. Walker got to know Muhammad as a Christian and a man. I remembered how one day, after he had worked in service with him, he said, "I like Muhammad. We have similar personalities and we both love Jehovah. I could see him as my son-in-law." I was thrilled to hear that because another young man Wanisha dated previously, Walker just did not care for. He genuinely liked Mo which was short for Muhammad. Within months, Mo had proposed. We hired Anita Broady, our spiritual sister and dear friend, who was a professional wedding coordinator. Walker and I were so excited for our daughter because she loved Muhammad and we could see how happy they were together.

Wanisha majored in Culinary Arts at Delaware County Technical School in Aston, Pennsylvania. From this field of arts, she became a prolific cake designer of creations such as school buses, Bibles, houses, and any type of thing her clients requested. Walker and I admired the young woman she became especially as a servant of the true God Jehovah and his precious son Jesus Christ. Wanisha had taken time out of her life to learn the truth based on what the Bible taught. This education based on the Bible taught her to rely on Jehovah's holy spirit so that she could delve into God's word individually. Wanisha learned how to look and pray to God for a man that wanted to walk in the footsteps of his son Jesus Christ. She found that in Muhammad.

Jaleesa, our youngest daughter also gave Muhammad her seal of approval. She was and still is very close to Wanisha. Jaleesa is a fearless regular pioneer and servant of

Jehovah God as well. She took on the tasks prayerfully to be educated based on Bible truths to individually come to know God and his son Jesus Christ. Walker and I were determined to set an example for our children. We wanted to teach them not the thoughts of men but the thoughts of Jehovah through his word the Bible. Jaleesa asked her dad once, "Daddy, who wrote the Bible? Was it God or men?" I remembered how Walker carefully responded, "Jaleesa, let's pray to Jehovah for the answer. We will do some research and we will discuss it at our family Bible study tomorrow." She was always spiritually minded, inquisitive, intelligent and a daddy's girl. I saw her immediately go to her bedroom. I heard Jaleesa praying to Jehovah for the answer.

At the time, Jaleesa was around 12 years old, and she enjoyed asking Bible questions. The next time we had our family Bible study, Walker asked Jaleesa if she had found the answer to her questions regarding who wrote the Bible? Was it God or men? She immediately responded, "After I prayed to Jehovah and did some research in *The Watchtower* magazine of March 2010, an article entitled, *The Bible Really Is God's Inspired Word* it stated, "The Bible writers 'spoke from God as they were borne along by holy spirit,' said the apostle Peter. (2 Peter 1:21) Hence, the apostle Paul could also describe the books of the Bible as 'holy writings,' which are able to make you wise for salvation through the faith in connection with Christ Jesus.'" (2 Timothy 3:15) It was through our Bible-based, Christian meetings at the Kingdom Hall, Walker had learned how to train his daughters to rely on Jehovah's holy spirit to help them through specific prayers to find the answers to life's questions. Jaleesa admired that quality about her father. She could see that same type of quality in Muhammad when Jaleesa met him. She knew Mo was the right man for her sister Wanisha.

The first time I met Muhammad was at Jaleesa's and Wanisha's dance recital. This event was held during the month of June 2014 at *Diane Matthews School of Dance Arts* in West Chester. Mo's silent, humble attitude reminded me of Walker in so many ways. Now that Wanisha and Mo had dated as a Christian couple, he proposed, and she accepted. Plans for their wedding was completed. Our family was excited as Anita got things organized. Finances were tight but we had saved and planned for our daughter's wedding day. Our entire family was excited for Wanisha and Muhammad.

After numerous shops and trying on a variety of wedding gowns Wanisha discovered a Sabrina Ann Bridal shop located in Ardmore, Pennsylvania. It is an intimate wedding salon specializing in designer once-worn, consignment and sample bridal gowns. It was there she found the perfect white wedding gown embroidered in lace and sequins on the top down to the waistline. From the waistline down was a white satin full pleaded attached skirt with pearl like buttons down the back and a full train that flowed. She also found a beautiful white vail to match the gown. Wanisha was ready for her wedding day, and Walker and I were thrilled.

On June 28, 2015, around 11:00 a.m., our house was filled with bridesmaids. There were makeup artists who carefully designed beautifully painted faces and eyes. Hairdressers curled crowns of hair arranged into upward styles. Beautiful pink gowns were displayed around our daughter's bedrooms for each bridesmaid that included Nisha, a gorgeous childhood friend that my children grew up with from Chester; Sheena, another stunning best friend of Wanisha and Jaleesa; Darlena, my daughters' beautiful cousin and best friend and their shy but gorgeous cousin LaShea. The ravishing Jaleesa filled the role as her sister's maid of honor. She wore a unique, aqua colored gown. These young women that served as Wanisha's bridesmaids were servants of God and looked like top models. I attempted to look my very best with the help of the makeup artist. It was a struggle amid all these runway models.

Walker went to check on Muhammad and his groomsmen. They got dressed and organized at the luxurious Dupont Hotel in downtown Wilmington, Delaware. Mo worked as an assistant manager at the time. Our very handsome, future son-in-law had become more like a beloved son to Walker. Mo wore a light gray tuxedo, white shirt, gray bowtie with a white carnation on his left lapel. His groomsmen included an array of Christian as well as handsome young men. The groomsmen were Evan, Ceyron, Ian, and Ron. They wore dark gray tuxedoes, white shirts, light gray bowties, and white carnations on their left lapels as well. Mo's best man was Leon. He wore a dark gray tuxedo, white shirt, with an aqua vest and bowtie that matched the maid of honor. The bridal party looked quite dapper that day all thanks to Jehovah.

Walker and I were an afterthought amid all these beautiful servants of God. My husband still pulled it off quite well. Walker wore a black tuxedo with a white shirt, gold bowtie and a white carnation in his left lapel. He looked so handsome. I wore a gold evening gown covered with sequins, with a small train that flowed behind me. A left wristband of flowers was included as well. Now that we were all dressed and groomed it was time to get into the limos for our daughter's special day of marriage to Muhammad.

This was a glorious day not just about the beautiful clothing, luxurious facilities, delectable food but it was about what Jehovah God as our Grand Creator had given us. He performed the first wedding or marital arrangement in the Garden of Eden when Eve was given to her husband Adam. We tried to imitate what God had taught us for man and woman to be joined together as husband and wife based on Genesis 2:22. That is why the wedding ceremony was held at one of our larger Kingdom Halls in Delaware. Anita made some outstanding arrangements with the owner of *The Waterfalls* in Claymont, Delaware where the reception was held. Beautiful renovations had just been completed at this location with a luxurious display for a wedding. Our family decided along with Anita that we would still have Wanisha and Muhammad's wedding at the Kingdom Hall. This is the location where we worshipped our God Jehovah under the rulership of Jesus Christ. There were not one piece of exorbitant furnishings or objects. Just simple, floral arrangements to maintain the dignity and honor of God's marital arrangement. We decided to show appreciation and respect for our family and friends of all races by having the reception at *The Waterfalls.*

It was now Sunday, June 28, 2014, around 5:00 p.m. Everyone had arrived for the wedding ceremony which included the bride and groom at the Kingdom Hall in

Wilmington, Delaware. Our spiritual son Joel Hendley served as the elder and ordained minister who performed the wedding ceremony for Wanisha and Muhammad. The groom along with his groomsmen stood firmly in front of the hall on the right side. The bridesmaids marched graciously up the aisle in their pink, peplum gowns with gold belts. Jaleesa marched in next with her aqua colored, peplum gown with a gold belt. There were two adorable flower girls named Saniya and Nyla who were Muhammad's nieces. They wore ornate white gowns with lace on top. The flower girls sprinkled flowers along the aisle on the left and right. Now it was time for Walker and me to walk up the aisle with our daughter the bride. I took Wanisha's left arm and Walker took her right arm. Grant Beauford read the beautiful words inspired by God at Genesis 2:22-23, "And Jehovah God built the rib that he had taken from the man into a woman, and he brought her to the man. Then the man said:

"This is at last bone of my bones
And flesh of my flesh.
This one will be called Woman,
Because from man she was taken." (NWT)

A piano arrangement played as we marched our daughter up the aisle to relinquish Wanisha to Muhammad. The piano music ended quietly. Cameras flashed as we arrived in front of Mo. Walker and I removed our arms discreetly and took our seats. Joel then asked, "Do you Muhammad Ali Bey in the presence of Jehovah God and these witnesses take Wanisha Suzzette Carter to be your wedded wife. To love and to cherish in accord with the divine law, as outlined in the holy scriptures for Christian husbands, for as long as you both shall live." Muhammad answered, "I do." Joel then asked our daughter, "Do you Wanisha Suzzette Carter in the presence of Jehovah God and these witnesses, take Muhammad Ali Bey to be your wedded husband, to love and to cherish and deeply respect in accordance with the divine law as outlined in the holy scriptures for Christian wives for as long as you both may live?" Wanisha excitedly responded, "I do." Brother Hendley then asked, "Who gives this woman to be married to this man?" Walker and I joined hands and stood up proudly and answered, "We do." Immediately, we took our seats again.

Joel continued with the wedding vows. Brother Hendley asked Muhammad to turn toward Wanisha as they repeated their vows to each other. Walker and I looked at each other as I remembered our wedding vows. We laughed along with the audience as Wanisha and Muhammad both were nervous which was common, but they got through their vows. Once their vows were completed Joel asked, "Are there rings to be exchanged?" Once the best man delivered the rings to the bridal couple the minister explained, "These rings are an outward and visible sign signifying unto all the uniting of this man and this woman are united in true matrimony. For as much as Muhammad Bey and Wanisha Carter coveted before Jehovah God and these witnesses to accept each other in wedlock. As an ordained minister by the authority conferred upon me by the holy scriptures and the state of Delaware, I pronounce that they are husband and wife together. 'What God has yoked together let no man put apart.' It is my pleasure to introduce to this marriage gathering Brother and Sister Bey." Brother Hendley forgot to tell Mo to kiss his wife. Audience members quickly reminded him. We all laughed as Muhammad was told to kiss his bride. They kissed and walked down the aisle as they rejoiced. A procession line was created for those that were not invited to the reception as Wanisha and Mo thanked everyone for sharing their special day.

Around 6:00 p.m., we arrived at *The Waterfall* in Claymontfor the wedding reception. The venue had just completed spectacular renovations. A magnificent waterfall cascaded in the front of the building upon our entrance. Within the foyer was white marvel flooring with a spalling fountain in the middle. Amazing glass chandeliers that sparkled throughout the ballroom. Thanks to Jehovah, Anita got us a great deal since the renovations had just been completed. The food was outstanding with a variety of cultures represented by such delicacies as jerk chicken, spring rolls, barbeque ribs, fried shrimp, various seafood, a medley of salads, roast beef, leg of lamb as well as an assortment of vegetables, desserts, and drinks. We wanted to show our family and friends how much we appreciated their support all thanks to our God Jehovah. After dinner when Muhammad and Wanisha had their first dance as husband and wife, our guests enjoyed dancing until the reception ended. Walker and finally got the chance as we enjoyed our special dances together. We were so thankful because it was a beautiful day.

I will never forget how happy Walker that night after the wedding and reception was over. I could tell he felt that it was one of his greatest accomplishments by being able to provide this type of wedding and reception for his oldest daughter. He had worked so hard, sometimes double shifts at PECO. Walker knew the strength and power to do these things were a gift from God. I loved that about him because Walker comprehended the origin of his power. He taught me and our daughters about this awe-inspiring power which comes from Jehovah God and his precious son Jesus Christ. This gave our family the foundation to live our lives to its greatest potential in our service to Almighty God.

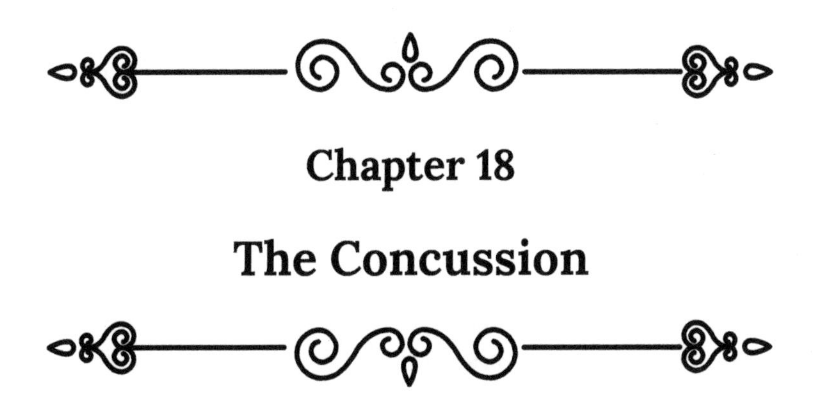

Chapter 18

The Concussion

On March 29, 2016, the sun was bright as it radiated 69th Street shopping area in Upper Darby, Pennsylvania. I had taken a break during my Metro Christian ministry work at 69th Street Transportation Center. We displayed Bible-based literature on carts so that people could take them free of charge. I also enjoyed shopping at the various stores on 69th Street. I enjoyed sharing Bible-based literature as I shopped. On my way out of a clothing store, I met this unusual looking man on a bench in the front of the store. I offered him a Bible tract. The way he responded seemed almost demonic as he screamed, "Get away from me. I don't want that." He looked at me with a cold-blooded, indurate look. I responded, "Well, you have a great day." I turned and headed down the sidewalk which was somewhat crowded. I felt dejected when all I wanted to do was give that man a hope for the future.

I was with another spiritual sister who rushed ahead of me as she spoke with another friend. With my shopping bag in one hand and my field service bag in my right hand, my foot turned from a crack in the sidewalk. I stumbled and fell head-on into the window of a nail shop. Blood flowed as I attempted to stand. Some people gathered to help me up. I went into the nail shop. The owner placed peroxide and bandages on the right side of my forehead where I had received a large gash to stop the blood flow. I appreciated everyone's assistance, but I just wanted to get home to Walker so that he could take me to the hospital. I stood up and said to the owner of the shop, "I think now that the bleeding has stopped, I would like to drive home to contact my husband about this injury. The pain started to be excruciating."

The sister assisted me to my car and asked, "Are you sure you will be alright to drive home by yourself?" I replied, "Yes. With Jehovah's help I should be okay." I called Walker on my cell phone before I left the parking lot. He answered immediately, "Hello, baby what's wrong?" Walker knew while I was in my ministry it was rare that I called him. With a bandage on my forehead and intense pain, I cried, "Walker, I had an accident." He quickly responded, "Are you okay?" Walker waited for my explanation,

"I fell into a store window. There was a large crack in the sidewalk. My foot turned and I fell head-on into the window." He asked in a state of panic, "Are you bleeding, and shouldn't you call an ambulance?" I responded with determination, "The lady who owns the store gave me peroxide and a bandage, so the bleeding has stopped." Walker then responded with the comforting words I wanted to hear, "I prefer you go to the hospital, but I want to take you. So, I'll meet you at our house." A reassured smile came across my face as I said, "Okay baby! I'll see you at the house." Tears rolled down my face as I backed my car out of the parking lot and drove home.

I arrived at our home just as Walker pulled up with his PECO truck. I jumped out of my car and ran into his arms. Walker's embrace brought me solace that everything would be alright. He held me tightly for a few seconds, looked at my forehead and asked frantically, "Baby, is your head hurting?" Before I responded Walker said, "We have to get you to the hospital." We got in my car and quickly headed to the hospital. I looked at Walker as I thought, "He is genuinely worried about me. My head is pounding. I started to feel a little better because my man was taking care of me. I knew everything would be alright. I never realized that this was the beginning of the end."

Walker and I arrived at the front desk of the emergency room. We both looked panicked. He anxiously said to the nurse, "Excuse me nurse. My wife fell into a store window. I think she has a concussion and in need of immediate help." I remained quiet as Walker took control of the situation. The nurse quickly responded, "We're going to take care of your wife. Can I see your insurance card?" I handed the nurse my card. She said, "Please have a seat and fill out this information. He filled out the form for me as my headache worsened. Walker returned the paperwork to the nurse's desk in the emergency room.

We sat in the emergency room for at least another half an hour. Another nurse came out and invited us into her office. I struggled to my feet as Walker assisted me. When we arrived in her office, I sat down slowly. He remained standing. The nurse introduced herself. Sat forward in her seat and looked directly into my eyes and then asked suspiciously, "Are you okay? You can tell me if your husband did this to you." I chuckled and explained sternly, "So, do you see any bruises on my husband? Trust me, if he had done this to me, he would be beat up as well. I don't play that!" I sat back in my chair with tremendous confidence. Walker quickly agreed, "That's for sure. I have more love and respect for my wife than that." The nurse could tell this was the truth as she smiled and said, "Alright Mrs. Carter. I'm happy to hear that. You can go and they will be right with you for a scan of your forehead." Walker and I both gave a sigh of relief as we left the nurse's office.

The pain from the cut on my forehead continued to be intense. I returned to my chair sluggishly. Walker saw the tears welled up in my eyes. The pain was severe. After about 45 minutes, a nurse invited me back for my scan. I was helped onto a cold, slightly uncomfortable stretcher. The scan was completed. They eventually returned me to the observation room. I received medication along with eight stitches. The doctor explained,

"Mrs. Carter, you have a severe concussion. Your husband will have to watch over you during the night because you could fall asleep and not wake up." I looked at the doctor and replied, "That sounds so scary." The doctor reminded me again of the seriousness of a concussion as we listened carefully.

When we arrived home from the hospital, Walker was so caring and helpful. He got very little sleep. Walker checked on me every few hours just to make sure I was alright. Our daughters helped with meals as well as family and friends. I felt Jehovah's tender love as it embraced me with delectable, home cooked meals prepared by my spiritual sisters as well. They prepared enough food to feed our family. I appreciated that since Walker returned to work. For weeks and months, I received treatments of therapy for my concussion. Family members like my brother Edward and twin sister Bernadette would take me to my doctor appointments. Walker and I, along with our daughters, were so thankful for everyone's loving support during this difficult time. We had no idea what still lied ahead for our family.

Two months later, I still struggled with my concussion. Headaches, double vision, vomiting, certain lighting in rooms bothered me, and I was often depressed. While at home one morning, before we got out of bed, Walker held me as I cried. Walker always led our family in prayer as the head of our household. His prayers became more powerful and endearing as he would call on Jehovah to get us through these critical times in Jesus' name.

I became self-contented that I would never take the lead in prayer over my husband's head. I could clearly see in the Bible that there was an arrangement God had established, "But I would have you know, that the head of every man is Christ; and the head of the woman is the man; and the head of Christ is God." 1 Corinthians 11:3 *(King James Version)* This gave me a source of respect and appreciation for the role that Jehovah God and his precious son Jesus Christ gave my husband. I loved it. Some women may have a problem with this scripture and its application. I didn't because it was clear that God created man first. He performed the first medical procedure as he took a rib from the man Adam and created his wife Eve as a complement to her husband based on Genesis 2:21-22 which states, "And the Lord God causes a deep sleep to fall upon Adam, and he slept; and he took one of ribs, and closed up the flesh instead thereof; And the rib, which the Lord God had taken from man, made he a woman, and brought her unto the man." Walker's loving nature and respect for God and me as his wife made those verses easy to apply and accept. We were determined to go on with Jehovah's help.

During these problematic situations with my concussion along with the fact that our 30th wedding anniversary would arrive on June 7th, 2016, we decided to go on a trip that we had planned for years but could not afford. Walker wanted to fulfill one of our dreams which was to take a cruise throughout the Mediterranean. Our cruise on Norwegian Cruise Lines was magnificent! We started from Barcelona, Spain to various parts of Italy which included Monte Carlo and Nice. During our seven-day cruise, we visited some of the most beautiful parts of the world.

We never realized this would be our last cruise together. I felt that is why Walker was so hell-bent to go on this cruise. Once we returned from our trip, I wrote an article on Hubpages.com as angelladywriter. I posted the beautiful photos of Naples, Italy, and our tour of the Pompeii *Excavation.* I also posted pictures of us in Rome, Florence, and Pisa, Italy. Pictures were also posted of Nice with its perfume factory and the beautiful Monte Carlo with an abundance of top designer shops such as Gucci and Versace. We loved Monte Carlo the most because of its spectacular views but we could not afford to shop there. I believed Walker was doing a bucket list of things before his death. That is why the time husbands and wives spend together should be precious and cherished because tomorrow isn't promised or guaranteed to any of us.

Chapter 19

The Devastating News that Changed Our Lives Forever

The night before I visited my family physician Dr. Morris McCray, I dreamed about the day I married Walker. I had a dream about the wedding vows we exchanged as we looked lovingly into each other's eyes. Within my dream, I remembered the birth of my children and how Walker held them in his arms each time as he thanked God for these precious gifts. He promised Jehovah in Jesus Christ name they would be raised to love and serve God. This dream featured precious, unforgettable memories. I asked myself the next morning, "What did this dream have to do with my doctor's appointment today?" This appointment was for a checkup based on the concussion I received a few weeks earlier. We soon discovered the connection.

We arrived at Dr. McCray's office in Chester. He was one of the first black doctors in Chester. Dr. McCray was our family physician since the birth of our children, and now our oldest daughter was almost 30 years of age. Walker and I admired him as a beloved doctor and friend. Once we were back in the examining, room I sat on the table. Walker sat in a chair across from me. Dr. McCray entered the room with a smile and said, "Good afternoon. I haven't seen you two for a while. Claudette, I see in my notes you have a concussion. When did this happen?" I replied, "March 29th, which was about two weeks ago." He looked at the cut on my forehead. Dr. McCray then checked my eyes as Walker looked on carefully. He asked with concern, "So, how do you feel?" I anxiously expressed, "I feel okay. My husband, family, and friends have been taking good care of me. I just thank God for them." Dr. McCray acknowledged, "That's good. I see you are going for therapy as well as neuropathy. Keep that up because your concussion was severe. I want you to check back with me in a few weeks." I agreed, "Okay, I will." I felt good about my visit with the doctor so far.

Dr. McCray for some mysterious reason turned slowly toward Walker. He carefully asked, "Coach Carter, how are you feeling?" Walker explained with a slight hesitation, "I've been feeling tired lately. And I have these lumps on each side of my lymph nodes."

Horrible thoughts rushed through my mind. I have never heard Walker say anything about lumps on the sides of his neck. What was this about? And why has he kept this a secret? The doctor placed his gloved hands on each side of Walker's neck. Dr. McCray's voice changed to a tone of concern, "That's a little suspicious. I'm going to recommend as soon as possible you go to an ear, nose, and throat specialist. His name is Dr. Ferri. His office is right here in Chester." I frowned at Walker as he looked away with a fake smile. Walker nods his head as he tried to reassure me, "It's going to be alright baby. Jehovah will help us through this." I wasn't convinced." I recalled a horrible smell like rotten meat came from Walker's breath at times. There was something wrong. I pretended to agree with him and stated, "I know baby. Jehovah got us through the concussion so far. He'll help us with whatever this is." But I still wasn't convinced.

Walker and I visited Dr. Ferri's office. He specialized in the ear, nose, and throat. During that visit, we received the tragic diagnosis of cancer. We were both debilitated. My strength was drained daily due to the concussion and Walker's strength weakened daily as well. The specialist recommended Riddle Hospital in Media, Pennsylvania for his cancer treatment. Dr. Ferri scheduled an appointment for Walker within two weeks for additional diagnosis and treatment.

What was revealed to Walker during his visit at Dr. Ferri's office did not deter him from his responsibility as an elder in the Christian congregation. He served Jehovah God diligently with the body of elders at Ardmore Congregation in Havertown, Pennsylvania. We were sent there to serve and preach the good news of God's Kingdom. Walker supported our daughters and me financially so that we could volunteer and serve as regular pioneers where we increased our volunteer hours to teach the Bible to others. We wanted to give Jehovah and his son Jesus Christ our very best service. This congregation needed help as they continued to teach people out of love about that Kingdom ruled by Jesus that would eliminate all of mankind's problems. We were all servants and volunteers. Not one person within any congregation of Jehovah's Witnesses received a salary as preachers of the good news. We do this out of love for people based on the example set by Jehovah and his son Jesus Christ.

The Sunday before Walker's appointment at Riddle Hospital, he gave a public talk at our local Kingdom Hall. Toward the conclusion of the public talk, Walker struggled as he read from the Bible at Psalms 91:11-16, "For he will give his angels a command concerning you, to guard you in all your ways." Walker hesitated for a moment. I started to pray as I held back the tears, "Oh, Jehovah help him." Walker swallowed; I could see the intense pain he experienced from his throat area. Walker continued as he read, "… God said: 'Because he has affection for me, I will rescue him. I will protect him because he knows my name. He will call on me, and I will answer him." I see his confidence in God grew as he struggled through those final words, "I will be with him in distress." ((*NWT)* Walker gave a slight grin and said, "This is the hope our God Jehovah gives us during tribulations." His confidence had been restored thanks to Jehovah. I watched him carefully as he left the platform and returned to his seat beside me. He smiled at me as I smiled back and thought, "I could tell my loving husband was suffering. Walker was determined to serve God to the best of his ability. Even through pain as the smell of rotting flesh protruded from his body. The fear of losing him was just too much to comprehend. I had to leave this in Jehovah's hands."

The next day after Walker struggled through his public talk, we arrived at Riddle Hospital located in Media. It was a division of Jefferson Hospital that treated cancer patients. A Dr. Jacobs dressed in his crisp white coat came into the room where Walker and I waited. He gave us a pleasant smile as he introduced himself and explained what he did within the center. Dr. Jacobs' expression suddenly changed in a sorrowful manner when he said, "I hate to be the bearer of bad news. But Walker, you have stage four cancer in your nasal cavity. We will have to aggressively treat this with radiation and chemotherapy." I held back the tears with all my might. Walker remained quiet and subdued. He seemed to have known this was inevitable. In a terrified voice I commented and then asked, "Dr. Jacobs, I can't lose my husband. Will he live? My daughters and I can't live without Walker. Will he get sick during these treatments?" I placed my hand to my forehead and screamed, "Jehovah, this is too much! Please help us. First it was my concussion and now Walker has cancer." I started to identify with Job in the Bible who dealt with so many tribulations all at once.

I appreciated the way Walker handled this situation. It was as if God gave him a voice of comfort that calmed me down. Walker knew I was fragile from my concussion, and he didn't want me to worry. I heard Walker say a silent prayer as he took me in his arms and said, "Baby, it's going to be okay. Jehovah will take care of us. We both have strong faith in God. If anything goes wrong, we have the hope of the resurrection based on Jesus' ransom sacrifice. We got to continue believing that." I looked back at Walker. There was a source of peace and assurance in his eyes. Without hesitation I defiantly responded, "Baby, you're right. I know we must have faith in Jehovah, but I don't want to think about you dying or the hope of the resurrection. Not now anyway." Walker hugged me tighter and then released me and explained, "We will pray and talk about it later." I understood because he needed to hear what Dr. Jacobs had to say about his treatments.

I appreciated Dr. Jacob's patience as well. I felt assured that he experienced these reactions quite often. Dr. Jacobs calmly explained, "We need to start your treatment of chemo and radiation within the next few days. Dr. Jessie DiNome is well known as our Medical Director of Jefferson Hospital Radiation Oncology of Riddle Hospital. I serve in Chemo Oncology and of course my name is Dr. Benjamin Jacobs. I just wanted both of you to know we will do our best to get Walker through these treatments. Let's schedule that appointment." He extended his hand to both me and Walker with a smile of reassurance. We both shook his hand as we were directed to the receptionist desk to schedule Walker's appointment to begin chemo and radiation treatments.

We returned home after our visit with Dr. Jacobs. Walker sat on the sofa siphoned of energy. He called his supervisor Bob Fowler. I sat down next to Walker as he shared the horrible news. Walker inhaled and then exhaled a deep breath and said, "Bob, it's not good news. I have stage four cancer in my nasal cavity." I could hear as Bob responded, "No. No. Walker I am so sorry to hear that." Walker replied, "I'm going to have to go out on sick leave." Bob responded, "No problem. Just remember that I am here as well as the company for you and your family." I took Walker's beautiful brown hand. My daughters and I would often tease Walker that he had the prettiest hands in the house. I would tell Walker that he could be a hand model. In retrospect, I never thought that one day those beautiful hands would be burned during his death. I held his left hand as I told Walker to thank Bob for his help as a PECO representative and friend. Walker repeated those words. I released his hand and ran upstairs to our bedroom to cry.

I didn't want to hear anymore of Walker's conversation with his supervisor. I thought about how Walker, admired Bob so much. They were like brothers, although Bob was his supervisor and Caucasian. Walker loved his job as a First Class Lineman at PECO. Now he would have to go on sick leave for months. This will be difficult for both of us. We also must tell our daughters Wanisha and Jaleesa as well as his mom. Walker's dad had passed over a year ago. Now, she could possibly lose a son. I would have to inform my family who helped me deal with a concussion. Unfortunately, we will have to tell them about Walker's cancer. "It's just too much," I cried.

It was Friday, June 22, 2016, when we received the tragic news from Dr. Jacobs about Walker's stage four cancer. The Cancer Center was a division of Riddle Hospital known as the Jefferson Radiation Oncology Center. They started his treatment aggressively with chemo and radiation. Walker's throat became burned with scars from these treatments. He could hardly swallow to eat. On Thursday, July 28, 2016, around 10:00 a.m. we returned to the cancer treatment center so that Walker could get a peg or eating tube. He did not receive it because of a blockage in his stomach area. I became upset with the doctor when I discovered that by 4:30 p.m., Walker was left with a tube stuck down his irritated throat after he had not eaten in a day. By the time I called her office to complain, the doctor had returned to remove the tube. I was thankful because Walker had grown weaker from lack of eating.

I brought him home so that he could attempt to eat a little soup which was painful for him to swallow. Walker was scheduled for a talk on the meeting that night at the Kingdome Hall. I also had a 5-minute part as well. Walker prayed for both of us as we gained strength from Jehovah to fulfill our parts that night. Jehovah helped us to endure through his sufferings from cancer treatments and my pain from a concussion. We wanted to give Jehovah something to bless.

Walker had weeks of radiation treatments every day from Monday to Friday. He also had chemotherapy and blood tests. I prayed often because of the detriment of the treatments on Walker's body. I watched him especially early in the mornings as I thought, "My poor baby." He struggled to walk because of his weakened condition due to lack of eating based on his bruised throat. Walker could hardly swallow because of the radiation. His weight diminished daily. He lost over 40 pounds. His love for God, family, and life, however, grew stronger. The treatments caused him to regurgitate his food. Walker's taste buds were also affected. He needed a feeding tube to survive. I continued to pray daily to help my baby through this process. Finally, we got the feeding machine with the tube.

One day after Walker's treatments of chemo and radiation, he decided to walk with me to the playground near our home. I knew he was not strong enough, but he was determined to go there. I wanted to get in the swing so that he could push me. As he did, I went higher and higher in the air. Suddenly, he stopped pushing me. I looked behind me and saw that Walker was bent over in pain. I jumped out of the swing and ran to him. I grabbed him around the waist. Walker was frail and fatigued. We headed back toward our home. Each step we took I thought, "Why did he have to suffer with this agonizing pain from cancer?" An attempted destroyer of true love existed. This destructive source tried to consume my love. But our love fought like a strong warrior. Look! To our right and left. Throngs of lovers surrounded us daily. Our love was strong, and it will defeat this intruder of our love. So many trials still laid ahead. Only Jehovah could help us through them.

About 6:00 a.m. on Saturday, August 13, 2016, I woke up to Walker crying as he sat on the side of the bed. I hesitated for a few minutes because of uncertainty. I prayed silently to Jehovah for Walker. I embraced him from behind as he cried, "Claudette I can't continue to do this. All these long hours. Six hours or more of chemo. It's killing me. This feeding tube is horrible. I hate that milky drink. I want to go out in field service to preach to people like I used to, but I just feel so weak. I'm tired and ..." I held Walker tighter as we rocked back and forth crying together. He had never complained like this before. I softly said, "Honey, it's going to work out with Jehovah's help. I'm so proud of you. You have been so strong. I love you so much."

There was suddenly a loud knock on our bedroom door. Wanisha, our oldest daughter, had spent the night. Her and Jaleesa rushed in. They knelt before Walker. Jaleesa cried, "Dad, Jehovah knows you are doing your best. We love you and God loves you too." The girls had obviously heard what their dad was concerned about. Normally, on Saturday, Walker would go out in field service together as a family. It was difficult for him to fulfill that role now. I considered how the radiation every day, from Monday to Friday, along with the chemo and blood tests had taken its toll on Walker. He would try to eat, and he continued to throw-up whatever he ate. I often discovered him sitting in complete darkness on the sofa in the family room. He stared with a blank look whenever he was hooked up to that feeding machine with the tube. The milky substance travelled into his body for nourishment which made him more depressed. I started to believe I was losing my baby.

The walls of our home felt as if they were closing in on us. I had to get Walker out of the house for a few hours. I hated to see him connected to that feeding tube in the dark with a blank stare. We decided to go out for dinner and a movie. The AMC Dine-In Painters Crossing in West Chester was our choice. We watched the afternoon showing of the movie *Ben-Hur,* which was a remake of the original. It starred Morgan Freeman and

Jack Huston as Judah Ben-Hur. We ordered food and drinks that were delivered to our seats. This was a fictional Bible-based story and we both thought the movie was okay. We just wanted to feel somewhat normal again.

On Monday, August 22, 2016, Walker went to chemo around 8:15 a.m. He was there for over six and a half hours. When I went to pick him up, I could see the redness around his throat was intense. Dr. Jacobs explained, "Walker should not be able to swallow or eat with his throat like this. Most people would be on liquid food only. His tolerance with pain is much higher than most people. It is nice to see that he is still up and about, although most people would be somewhere curled up in bed." I was proud of Walker and how he had endured these treatments and the pain.

On September 19, 2016, Walker completed his treatments all thanks to Jehovah. He was given an award that stated, "*Certificate of Merit* for the successful completion of radiation therapy treatment with determination, positive attitude, and courage. Thanks for your placing, your care, confidence, and trust in our hands." This certificate was from Jefferson Radiation Oncology Center at Riddle Radiation Oncology Department Physicians and Staff -- Dr. Jessie DiNome, Terry, Jackie, Dawn, Alan, Marianne, Mary, Chau, and Princess. Our daughter Jaleesa created a shirt for her dad on this special occasion which expressed on the front, "I'm done!" On the back was Psalms 136. "Give thanks to Jehovah for he is good; His loyal love endures forever." (NWT) Walker even rang a bell on his way out of the door to signal he had successfully completed these treatments. We all rejoiced and thanked God that this part of his life was over. We thought Walker was on his way to continuous healing so that he could live. Once again, we were wrong.

Now that Walker completed his chemo and radiation treatments, a few weeks later, we decided to take the advice of our spiritual daughter Roxanne Hendley. She advised us to contact Wendy Fulford in Philadelphia who practiced Iridology and Sclerology sessions. She explained how, "Your eyes have answers for you!" This explanation was also given by Mrs. Fulford, "Through the eyes, one can tell the functioning of the internal body systems and organs; your eyes record this information in an organized and natural way." This information could possibly be used for herbal treatment which is another solution to cancer treatment. It was explained that Iridology and Sclerology is not like such things as palm readings or other forms of witchcraft. It is the use of a body organ such as the eye given to us by our Creator to investigate for logical answers and health concerns within our bodies. Iridology was also explained as the inspection of the iris of the eye as an aide in determining a person's state of health or in assessing a health problem.

Wendy does not claim to be a medical doctor but is certified in the study of the eyes and effects of cancer and other diseases for numerous years. This drew Walker's interest. We also maintained a circumspect attitude because there were so many scams of cancer cures, holistic care and various herbal treatments for cancer that were so prevalent. These sessions helped Walker with the burns around his neck from the chemo and radiation treatments. His diet also improved to the point that Walker started to gain some of his weight back. Through various herbs, Walker's body started to heal itself naturally. We thanked Jehovah daily as Walker regained his health and strength.

By January 2017, Walker had returned to work at PECO full time. He was thrilled to be back at work. Walker missed his supervisor Bob and the other linemen. His laughter and joy returned in the ministry as well. We knew that it was Jehovah God that helped him through these difficult months of illness. We struggled financially during his cancer treatments and my concussion treatments. Now, we both could see that bright light at the end of that dark tunnel.

Chapter 20

His Tragic Death After We Celebrated Our 31st Anniversary

For our 31st wedding anniversary, Walker and I went to Manhattan, New York. We stayed at the beautiful Millennium Hilton New York which was surrounded by Broadway theaters. Major musicals such as *The Lion King, Hamilton* and *Phantom of the Opera* surrounded us. Our first day out in New York, we rode in an open sky tour bus. We toured Times Square, Rockefeller Center, Empire State Building, and other areas such as the Bronx and Harlem. Because you can hop-on-hop-off, Walker and I decided to go to The Apollo Theater in New York. The publication *Apollo Ain't Nothing Like the Real Thing* described it this way: The Apollo stands virtually peerless in its tradition of hosting emerging talent as well as established artists. Long before shows such as *American Idol* and *Star Search, Amateur Night* at the Apollo helped to catapult unknown performers to superstardom. Such popular artists as James Brown, the Jackson Five, Ella Fitzgerald, and countless others launched their careers there.

During that week of our 31st wedding anniversary--June 6 through Friday, June 10, 2016, Walker and I were able to catch a live recording of *Amateur Night* at The Apollo Theater which was hosted by Steve Harvey with co-host Adrienne Bailon. It was hilarious as we sat in the audience and cheered for these very talented artists. Walker was captured on camera as he stood up and applauded for a very talented singer named Nadia Wilkes. We had fun that night at the Apollo.

Tuesday, June 7, 2016, was our anniversary. We had a full day planned. We started out with dinner at one of Walker's favorite restaurants in New York--Carmine's. He enjoyed the piled high eggplant parmigiana. I had the delectable surf and turf platter with the ribeye steak and lobster tail. We enjoyed our dinner so much. After dinner we went back to the hotel, got an hour nap with great anticipation for the evening plans on our anniversary.

We had tickets to go see an award-winning musical. Walker and I had been through so much to get these tickets. We obtained four tickets including two for our friends a few months before our anniversary. After I reviewed the tickets, I discovered they were for a *Hamilton* musical that would be performed in Chicago. We tried to return those tickets but was unable to. Finally, I was able to sell them online. We desperately wanted to see this musical because of the rave reviews it had received. Within a week before our anniversary, I obtained four tickets for the New York show. We decided to keep our promise for our friends and spiritual brother and sister Aaronda and Grant. I can recall I had four tickets in my hand. I gave them two tickets and I kept two. I handed our two tickets to the usher who seated us in the back row of the orchestra area. The excitement within my belly collapsed when I looked up and saw Aaronda and Grant in the best seats in the house. I immediately turned to Walker and said, "Why do they have the best seats. I want those seats!" He responded with his favorite reply, "Calm down, baby. Calm down." Walker decided that we should give them the best seats which were in an opera box above the audience with only a few people. I was so disappointed that we gave them the best seats, but Walker was thrilled to see Grant and Aaronda enjoy the musical which they both looked forward to as well.

Walker was so happy to see how much each of us enjoyed *Hamilton* that night. He once again checked off his list of love for others and humility as his time drew shorter. Even as the end of Walker's life was drawing near, he tried to walk in the footsteps of Jesus Christ who was taught by his Father Jehovah God how to give his very best.

Jehovah could have sent any of his angelic sons in heaven which consist of "legions of angels" based on Matthew 26:53 in the holy scriptures. But Jehovah God sent his very best, Jesus Christ, "Who is the image of the invisible God, the firstborn of every creature. For it pleased the Father that in him should all fullness dwell;" Colossians 1:15,19 (*King James Version*) Walker wanted our friends Aaronda and Grant to have the very best seats that he could afford. I can't say that I agreed but Walker was happy with his decision. I prayed and adjusted my attitude as well. It was still a wonderful day.

We returned to our hotel after Aaronda and Grant thanked us for the great seats to the *Hamilton* musical. We hugged them as they returned to their car to go back home in Pennsylvania. I was still a little pissed, but I didn't want to spoil the remainder of our anniversary celebration. Walker held me in his strong, loving arms which was a source of comfort. In a low voice, he said, "Baby this has been the best vacation we have been on in a long time. For our thirty-first wedding anniversary, we got to see so much. I feel if I never return to New York again, I'll be alright." I looked at him and said, "That's an odd way to put it. But I'm glad to hear how much you enjoyed this trip." I couldn't help but think, "Why, did he say that?" It was like an inevitable foreshadowing that Walker would never return to New York.

Walker gently kissed me as I kissed him back. We made love that night as husband and wife as if it was our last anniversary together. He was amazing. Walker had returned to his youthful vigor. He gained some of his weight back with the complement of a six pack. Walker's stamina was astounding. It was as if he tried to forewarn me that this would be the last time we made love because his death was eminent. Afterwards, we laughed as I explained, "Baby, we don't need to do it again for another week or so because that was awesome." Walker laughed but never responded. I thought, "That's odd." He released me from his arms, turned over and fell asleep.

The next day Walker and I returned from New York. When we arrived home, Kevin Kessler, one of his best teenage friends visited. Walker always enjoyed their laughter and jokes together. Kevin would tell such experiences as when Chester High School's newspaper did a story entitled, *Chester High's Own Brian Song.* This award-winning movie was based on the true story of Brian Piccolo played by (James Caan) and Gale Sayers played by (Billy Dee Williams). Piccolo and Sayers were teammates on the mid-1960s Chicago Bears. At a time when professional football still bears a certain amount of race-based segregation, the growing friendship between the white Piccolo and the black Sayers, as well as their wives, Joy (Shelley Fabares) and Linda (Judy Pace), became a symbol of harmony during the civil rights era. That bond grows stronger still when Piccolo receives some shattering and unexpected news.

I will never forget the way we laughed as Kevin and Walker bantered back and forth about this *Brian Song* article. I listened carefully as Walker laughed and said, "Yeah. I told you about the article and asked what you thought about it?" Kevin responded, "So, let me get something straight. I'm Brian Piccolo and you're Gayle Sayers, right? Walker replied, "Yes." Kevin laughed and said, "Well, that sucks." Walker asked, "How's that?" Kevin responded, "Well, for the first time it doesn't pay to be white." Walker laughed and asked, "How's that?" Kevin replied, "Because the white guy dies." The room was filled with explosive laughter by the three of us. Based on this true story in the movie; Piccolo who was white, died after a battle with cancer. Walker and I enjoyed Kevin's perspective of this true story and many other experiences they shared over the past 50 or more years. Their race never mattered to them regardless of what Walker's black friends or Kevin's white friends thought. I was thankful they got the privilege to hang out together before Kevin left and returned home to California. This would be their last time together as friends.

Chapter 21

A Void Existed on the Earth the Day of Walker's Death

On Tuesday, June 20, 2017, Walker had an appointment with Wendy Fulford in Philadelphia around 10:00 a.m. Walker wanted to get his Iridology and Sclerology sessions in before work at 3:00 p.m. A lot of prayers to Jehovah, where he created the eyes so that Wendy could see "the functioning of internal body systems and organs" as well as reflexology, herbs, and a proper diet rejuvenated Walker. The burns around his throat healed, and Walker was thrilled that he had gained even more of his weight back. I started to recognize my husband again. Walker was so happy spiritually and physically. We were amazed how God created our bodies so that they would gradually heal even from chemo and radiation treatments.

After the treatments at Mrs. Fulford's office, Walker and I headed home. He was so excited to be back at work as a First Class Lineman at PECO Energy. Walker had only been back about six months since January of that year. He missed Bob, the other linemen, and coworkers at the company. Walker loved his job. He enjoyed driving his bucket truck which allowed him to be called at a moment's notice for electrical emergencies especially when transformers were damaged. Entire neighborhoods would be in darkness until Walker, or any lineman, came to the rescue. I think he just liked helping people and his job enabled him to do that.

We laughed when we arrived home because of the somewhat muddy walkway. Walker started to remove the slate that was placed when we first moved into our home. His good friend Spike assisted Walker in that previous project. Now it was time for a new walkway which Walker attempted to replace. It was never completed by him.

Walker rushed upstairs, changed his clothes into a work uniform which consisted of an orange 100% cotton t-shirt and heavy blue jeans. Regardless of how many times I washed these items, the smell from the electrical poles remained in them. I walked out on the porch behind Walker. He kissed me as the smell from his t-shirt lingered. He headed toward the truck that was parked in the front of our house. Suddenly, Walker turned and reminded me as he stood in the muddy walkway, "Oh, don't forget. In about thirty minutes, I'll meet you down at Ace Hardware to get the bricks for this walkway." I nodded my head and said, "Okay. I'll see you there." Walker got into his truck and left for work. I watched him as he drove away.

About a half and hour later, I met Walker at Ace Hardware. It was only five minutes from our home. We decided on the brick pattern we wanted which didn't take us long. Walker had already checked in with his supervisor, but he still was anxious to return to work. Walker kissed me again which was strange, but I could see the joy in his eyes as he drove away. I returned to my car and headed home. I reminisced often about that last kiss and encounter with Walker. I had no idea the last time I would see Walker alive would be at Ace Hardware. My only thought when I left the store that day was I must get back home and prepare his favorite meal which was turkey wings. Usually, around 7:30 p.m. Walker would come home for dinner when he worked second shift. After I completed dinner, I was exhausted after our drive to Philadelphia for Walker's treatments. I got in the bed a little before 7:00 p.m. Many days I wished that I waited for Walker and had dinner with him. I was clueless about what would happen within the next ten hours which would be devastating.

The strangest thing occurred with our oldest daughter Wanisha. During that time, she lived in Delaware with her husband Muhammad. Wanisha can look through our home's security camera on an app from her telephone. That night, Wanisha watched Walker through our security camera around 7:45 p.m. on June 20, 2017. He was sitting on the sofa in the family room eating his dinner. That would be the last time she saw her dad alive.

I slept through Walker's dinner break which I regret. It was normal for him to decide to work a double shift due to electrical outages especially during the summer months whenever storms developed. Bob was possibly the last one to speak with him. During a break before Walker went out to the sight where he tragically died, Bob said he spoke with him around four that morning. It was later explained to me that possibly before 5:00 a.m., my wonderful husband and father of our children was electrocuted while in the bucket of the truck. Walker was discovered by a Haverford Township, Pennsylvania police officer. He saw the truck running but no response from anyone when the officer called out. Once he used his flashlight, the officer saw Walker's body slumped over tragically, deceased in the bucket. He contacted PECO. Bob and other co-workers arrived on the scene. Walker's body was removed and taken to the Medical Examiner's office.

I know a tremendous hole was left in my heart as well as family and friends. It was shocking because Walker had struggled through stage four cancer and survived. For him to die tragically months later, it was just too unbearable. He was a faithful servant of Jehovah God as he walked in the footsteps of Jesus by imitating and applying what the Bible taught. Walker was an imperfect man but a lover of God. I imagined that Jehovah God looked down from heaven that morning and saw the breath of life cease within his body. The memory of Walker now lies securely with Jehovah. Just as Jesus resurrected Lazarus by praying to his Father in order that God's holy spirit would give him the power at John 11:39-44, "Jesus said: 'Take the stone away.' Martha, the sister of the deceased, said to him: 'Lord by now he must smell, for it has been four days.' Jesus said to her: 'Did I not tell you that if you would believe you would see the glory of God?' So, they took the stone away. Then Jesus raised his eyes heavenward and said: 'Father, I thank you that you have heard me. True, I knew that you always hear me; but I spoke on account of the crowd standing around, so that they may believe that you sent me.' When he had said these things, he cried out with a loud voice: 'Lazarus, come out!' The man who had been dead came out with his feet and hands bound with wrappings, and his face was wrapped with a cloth. Jesus said to them: 'Free him and let him go.'" *(NWT)* My faith is strengthened that Walker will be resurrected just as Jehovah gave Jesus the power to resurrect Lazarus. We look forward to seeing Walker a beloved husband, father, brother, and friend again.

There was a void that penetrated the hearts of hundreds of thousands of people as the word of Walker's death was announced throughout the United States and around the world. He was a part of a loving worldwide brotherhood of more than 8 million Jehovah's Witnesses. Walker is missed and was such a major part of PECO Energy, Exelon out of Chicago, Widener University and Chester High School. Based on the hope of the resurrection, Walker will walk this earth again one day in the future because God cannot lie.

Chapter 22

The Revelation of Walker's Death

My daughter Jaleesa and I continued to cry as Bob and the State Trooper looked on with pity. I stopped for a few moments and thought as tears streamed down my face, "We must call Wanisha to let her know before someone else does. Otherwise, she'll be devastated." Jaleesa ran back upstairs to grab her cell phone. She called Wanisha but there was no response. We did not want to leave a message which could have caused tremendous suspicion by her and Mo. Bob immediately responded, "If you can't reach your daughter, I'll be happy to drive you to her house. It's no problem." With tears in my eyes, I looked at Bob and said, "Thank you so much. We really need to let Wanisha know ourselves. Thanks again." Jaleesa and I struggled up the stairs to get showered and dressed. I thought, "How loving this was on Bob's part because both Jaleesa and I were too distraught to drive, and he could see that. Now I can understand why Walker had so much respect, love, and appreciation for Bob as his friend and supervisor.

We rode down to Wanisha and Muhammad's house in Delaware to reveal this tragic news about her dad's death. I rode in the back seat of Bob's truck as Jaleesa rode in the front seat. I contacted Wendy Fulford and my cousin Robert who contacted others in our congregation. On the way to Wanisha's house on 95 south, we ran into a traffic jam. We were only a half a mile from my daughter's exit, so Bob was able to utilize the shoulder of the highway. I thought it's vital I reach my child with this horrible news before someone else does.

We arrived at Wanisha's house about a half an hour later. I noticed our spiritual daughter Nisha Williams was sitting on the steps of my daughter's house. Jaleesa called Nisha and asked her to meet us there. She had no clue what was going on. When I got out of the truck Nisha asked, "Mom, what is going on? When Jaleesa called, she didn't tell me what was going on. What is it?" I turned from Nisha without a reply. I embraced her as Jaleesa knocked loudly on Wanisha's front door. We started to call out to my daughter because she slept with a sound machine which made it difficult for her to hear. Suddenly,

Muhammad opened the front door. We entered their home. Jaleesa ran to hug Wanisha as she came down the stairs. I sat on their sofa and just started to cry profusely. Wanisha asked, "What's going on?" I said, "Your father died this morning. He was killed on his job." Nisha helplessly fell to the floor as she cried. Muhammad, Wanisha, and Jaleesa gathered as they all screamed, "No. No." We cried and comforted each other as Bob waited for us to return outside.

When Bob brought us back home, the news of Walker's death had been revealed throughout the area as well as throughout Exelon, PECO, and Widener University. Family members, brothers and sisters from our Kingdom Halls, friends, corporate members, and co-workers of Walker, gathered to support us. Telephone calls, texts, cards, food, and flowers started to pour in. The demonstration of love was overwhelming. Our family was strengthened and encouraged. Bernadette, her daughter Chante, granddaughter LeShae, nieces Kasia and her daughter Kashyia helped organized everything that came within the house.

Our Kingdom Hall brothers and sisters were there to help organize the second memorial service along with the food for that special event. There were just too many people to have just one funeral service. I was thankful they took care of that and many other responsibilities which encouraged us spiritually. I was too distraught after Walker's death to get out of bed some days. Jehovah God provided just what we needed when we needed it. We were so thankful.

Within a day or so after Walker's death, Craig Adams, now retired, served as President and CEO of PECO. He lovingly visited our home and gathered his team of corporate leaders which included Mike Innocenzo, who currently serves as President of PECO. Craig and Mike organized Jen Hana, Bob Fowler, Mary Knick, Wendy Sill, union leaders and co-workers from various departments of PECO to help our family through this formidable time. They provided for Jen, who served in management over Walker and the other linemen. She became like a dear sister. Jen helped us make funeral arrangements, helped decide on a location for dinner after the funeral and just lovingly supported us. Jen was like a sister from another mother. Bob was there for us as well through thick and thin. Each of those PECO employees were and still are dear friends to my daughters and me. They were a blessing from Jehovah God, and I will never forget their loving support during this critical time.

A few days after Walker's death, I woke up around 4:30 a.m. listening for his truck. Around this time, I got used to Walker either coming home if he was on third shift or worked a double. Then I realized that Walker died and would no longer come home. I recalled some of the good times Walker and I shared together. A memorable quote from a Tyler Perry movie related to our relationship as husband and wife, we had a love so strong. It just seemed like we were one. There were those moments when I just laid my head on his chest. And then I realized that his heartbeat matched mine. I have had an opportunity that few people ever get on this earth. God has blessed me with a man that was designed just for me. I have been blessed and divinely favored.

Memories of our wedding day flashed in my mind when we danced together slowly as we kissed. I laughed as I remembered how proud I was of my $19 zirconia ring on our wedding day. I wore that ring and presented it to others as if it was worth a million dollars. We were so thrilled to be married as Walker and I left the reception hall after our wedding to start our lives together. Reality stifled my dreams because the partner and lover no longer shared these illusions. I missed every single touch, kiss, and smile. Walker's memorial service would be held within a few days. I prayed constantly to Jehovah God in Jesus name for help to get through this service and he heard and answered my prayers.

Chapter 23

The Funeral and Memorial Services for Walker

On Friday, June 23, 2017, after deciding on arrangements, our family went to view Walker's body at the Minshall Shropshire-Bleyler Funeral Home in Middletown Twp, Media. It was around 4:00 p.m. when we arrived. Only immediate family members and Jen from PECO attended. This was the first time I saw Walker after his death. I could discern from a distance that the funeral director placed him in a beautiful black coffin with a variety of flowers surrounding it. Walker looked as though he was sleeping peacefully on a white satin pillow within the casket. I walked slowly and when I arrived, Walker looked so distinguished and handsome. White gloves covered his hands because they were burned severely. The tragic death of electrocution did not rob Walker of his dignity and appearance.

In retrospect, Walker picked this black pinstripe suit with a pink shirt and pink tie a few weeks before his death. Out of all the suits he owned Walker said, "I don't have a black pinstripe suit with a pink shirt and tie. I have various colors and combinations but not that." During my ministry at 69th Street, in Upper Darby, I decided to check out some of the men's wear shops. The very first time after Walker said this, I discovered this exact suit with the pink tie and shirt in a store window. I immediately called and advised him of this discovery. The next day after work, Walker and I drove up to purchase this outfit. It was perfectly tailored to fit him. A few days later, Walker brought the suit home and wore it to our Kingdom Hall of Jehovah's Witnesses that Sunday. He looked so fine in this black pinstripe suit with pink tie and shirt. Other sisters and brothers commented on how nice Walker looked. He was so elated. If was as if Walker was saying, "Upon my death I will wear this outfit." Walker and I do not believe based on the Bible in predestination. Ecclesiastes 9:11 reveals "… nor do those with knowledge always have success, because time and unexpected events overtake them all." (*New World Translation of the Holy Scriptures)* Walker's death was a tragic accident that occurred unfortunately.

My family gathered around the coffin with eyes full of tears. Bernadette, Doris, and Janie were the three of my sisters that were present for the viewing. My nieces Kasia and her daughter Kashya attended as well. They created an obituary and video for the funeral service. I appreciated everything my family and friends did because it was just too overwhelming for the girls and I to even comprehend what to write or organize. I was so thankful for my family and friends.

I noticed that Jen arrived to view Walker's body. She was tall with dark brown hair. Jen reminded me of George Clooney's wife, a beautiful, intelligent, statuesque woman. She was more than a co-worker and friend to Walker and our family. I had never met Jen previously until Walker's death. She became like a close sister to our family during this difficult time. Jen worked diligently with my daughters and I to make sure everything for the funeral and repass was taken care of financially by the company. We appreciated that so much because Walker's death was unexpected, and finances were far and few. As soon as Jen caught sight of him in the coffin, she broke out in tears. I tried to remain strong, but it was too much for both Jen and I. David's expressions at 1 Samuel 30:4 were appropriate once he saw the destruction of his city. David's family was also taken captive, "So David and the men with him began weeping loudly until they had no strength left to weep." *(NWT)* To see how Jen wept broke my heart as we embraced and cried together. I became weak and lacked strength as we approached the casket again.

Saturday, June 24, 2017, was the day of the first funeral service. Our family planned one specifically for the employees of PECO and Exelon. Employees and previous staff members and coaches from Widener University also attended. Friends of our family as well as classmates from Chester High School attended this service. Walker's family included Walker's mom Susie, sister Ocie, brothers Darryl, David, Sam, Bobby, and Steve and their wives Marie and Robin along with a host of our aunts, cousins, nieces, and nephews also attended this first funeral service. My brothers, sisters, nieces, and nephews supported us as well during this first funeral arrangement.

In Walker's memory, there were two white and blue PECO trucks with their buckets raised in the air. They were displayed on the funeral home's lawn in his memory as a lineman. Hundreds of people stood outside as they waited for the service which started around 10:00 a.m. Tears filled my eyes as my daughters Jaleesa, Wanisha, son-in-law Mo, and I arrived in the limousine. The loving support from people of all backgrounds was tremendous.

Our family never expected that we would line up in the front of the funeral home beside Walker's casket. My daughters, son-in-law, and Walker's family faithfully endured the hundreds of handshakes and condolences from each visitor that day before the memorial talk was given. I appreciated and loved each of them for that. After more than 500 passed through our line, it was time for the special, Bible-based, memorial talk.

Dan Braxton, an elder and close friend of our family, gave the memorial talk. I loved how he focused on the wonderful, realistic hope our family has for the future. From the scriptures, he revealed how we would see Walker again based on the awe-inspiring promise of a resurrection by Jehovah God through his son Jesus Christ. Dan read and requested that everyone joined him in their Bibles at such scriptures as John 5:25-28 which explained, "Most truly I say to you, the hour is coming, and it is now, when the dead will hear the voice of the Son of God, and those who have paid attention will live. For just as the Father has life in himself, so he has granted also to the Son to have life in himself. And he has given him authority to do judging, because he is the Son of man. Do not be amazed at this, for the hour is coming in which all those in the memorial tombs will hear his voice and come out..." *(NWT)* Brother Braxton concluded with Revelation 21:4 which described the type of life here on earth that Walker believed he will be resurrected into. A world with no sickness, death, pain, or sorrow. We look forward to seeing Walker in paradise on earth.

The funeral service for Walker was encouraging. Afterward, a repass was planned at the *Best Western Plus Concordville Hotel.* Family, friends, corporate leaders, and co-workers of PECO attended. A delicious meal of surf and turf was served. I wanted the best food and facilities in Walker's memory as I prayed the pain of his death would lessen. I was wrong because the whole day remained a blur. I missed him so much.

On Saturday, July 1, 2017, at 1:00 pm the second memorial service was held. Based on Walker's beliefs and will, he requested to be cremated after the first funeral service. Walker had faith in God that whether he was in the grave or cremated, the resurrection hope is possible. We have to consider how humans that have died hundreds of years ago, turned back to dust or skeletal remains. Still, Jehovah has the power based on his holy spirit which can be given to his son Jesus Christ, in order that our dead loved ones can and will be resurrected back to life. Our Grand Creator proved the reality of this hope through the resurrection of his son Jesus, Lazarus, and the widow of Nain's son. (1 Corinthians 15:12-21, John 11: 38-44 and Luke 7:11-15)

The second memorial service was held for our spiritual brothers and sisters, family, and friends throughout the Delaware Valley area. Both Walker and I have large families that could not attend the first service since it was scheduled less than a week after his death. It was held at Kingdom Hall of Jehovah's Witnesses in Wilmington, Delaware. Hundreds of people attended this service as well. They came from the Carolinas, Maryland, Philadelphia, New Jersey, New York, and other major cities. When my daughters, son-in-law, and I entered the Kingdom Hall, there was such a genuine source of love and consolation. We received hugs and words of encouragement. Bernadette was mistaken for me, so she received a tremendous amount of love as well. That is the type of love we receive in Jehovah's worldwide organization of servants.

Jim Marquisette, our spiritual brother and friend, gave the second memorial talk. Walker looked up to him as a strong spiritually-minded, father figure. We opened the service with a beautiful song that focused on the hope of the resurrection. The obituary was read by brother Jeremy Branch who served as Chairman. The memorial talk was then given by brother Marquisette. This talk consisted of scriptures filled with hope such as John 5:28,29, Psalms 37:10,11, and Revelation 21:3,4.

I tried to stand as they sang the last song with such faith strengthening words as: "Just see yourself, just see me too;" I looked at Walker's beautiful portrait that was displayed on an easel in front of the Kingdome Hall. Tears consumed my face as I tried to utter the words, "Just see us all in a world that is new. Think how you'll feel, how it will be..." I couldn't finish the words. They were just too realistic as I remembered Walker was gone and the memory of him is secure in Jehovah's memory. When the time comes Walker will be resurrected. An inspirational prayer was given to remind our family of our wonderful hope for the future. Numerous friends and family lined up again as we sat to greet them. It was just too many people, so eventually I escaped out of the side door with my eyes full of tears. I was just too overwhelmed. How thankful I was that Jehovah helped our family through both services.

Chapter 24

Accolades Created for Walker by PECO and Widener University

The compassion demonstrated by PECO under Craig Adams, who served as president until March 2018, was admirable. After Walker's death, Craig was there as a good friend. Denis O'Brien, senior executive vice president of Exelon Corporation and CEO of Utilities described Adams this way: "Leaders like Craig don't come around very often," said O'Brien. "Even beyond his focus on operational excellence and dedication to improving the customer experience, he was one of the most accessible CEOs I've ever seen." Upon reading this about Craig Adams, I had to agree. I could call Craig anytime about my concerns and he responded. This approach of genuine concern for my daughters and I flowed throughout the company because of Craig's leadership. When Mike replaced Craig as president of PECO Energy, he demonstrated the same genuine care for my daughters and I. This was a blessing from God, and we were so thankful. It was as if they understood the pain in my heart because I missed and loved Walker so much. Jen and Bob became close friends as well that I can call on. All these employees as well as numerous others have been a blessing to our family now that Walker has been deceased for over four years.

A year later, on June 21, 2018, the Linemen of PECO along with corporate leaders and other employees designed a memorial that was dedicated in Walker's memory. It was established at the PECO Energy facility in Eddystone, Pennsylvania. It still exists today with an impactful photo of Walker in his truck which the company retired as well. Picturesque flowers of various colors surrounded the gazebo setting where linemen can sit and have lunch as other linemen are dispatched daily.

Unfortunately, Jaleesa, Wanisha, Muhammad, and me were out of town because of the one-year anniversary of Walker's death. We had no idea PECO planned to do this. Later, during the fall, an honorary breakfast was given so that our family and other employees could be a part of this dedication. Mike, now president of PECO, shared an experience of how he discovered who Walker Carter was. Mike said, "When

I started attending Widener University, I heard about this great athlete Walker Carter who attended Widener. Along with his team, Widener won a national championship in football. Walker was also famous for winning championships in track and field. When I came to PECO I continued to hear about Walker Carter. I finally got to meet him one day when I rode along with him in his PECO truck. I could see why so many people admired him. Walker was a great guy." I laughed when Mike shared this experience during the dedication ceremony. It was a beautiful experience for my children and I, which reminded us of how much Walker was respected, loved, and appreciated. He was taught by Jehovah to love and respect others which he tried to practice. It was obvious people appreciated that about him.

On October 12, 2018, at the Springfield Country Club in Springfield, Pennsylvania, Widener University held an Athletic Hall of Fame Induction ceremony. Walker was inducted along with other athletes such as Lauren Lucci for shot put championships, William "Red" Polluck for his outstanding skills in football, Ron Hodges for his outstanding achievements in football and track and field, Kate L'Armand a distinguished MAC champion in the field of athletics, and Pete Morrison for his outstanding achievements in baseball. The 1977-1978 men's basketball team was also recognized for their national championship victory. This event brought tears to my eyes as Coach Bob Young read Walker's accomplishments during his tenure at Widener University. The touchdowns as a wide receiver in a national championship game. With Bill Manlove as head coach, along with Bob Young, Walker, numerous other coaches, and team members Widener won another national title in football. Walker also became an outstanding athlete in track and field. That night, I made a brief speech as I humbly accepted this Hall of Fame award in Walker's memory with my family and friends' support. On the upper level of the Schwartz Center at Widener is a display of Widener's winning players, coaches, and staff.

On June 21, 2019, Chester Arts and Culture with Laurie Zierer as Executive Director for the center, presented a mini docudrama on Walker "Baby" Carter. I added "Baby" because that is what I called Walker. He was my baby. PECO Energy funded this project as Butch Slaughter served as director of this film. Amanda and her husband were the camera crew that filmed the production. Butch described the purpose of this docudrama, "The purpose of sharing life's experiences on such individuals as Walker is that these stories are the beginning and the end of this project called *Chester Made.* We collected hundreds on the chestercity.com website. These stories gathered in Chester helped to create a *Cultural Asset Map.* The results of the story gathering furthers the understanding of the power and value of the arts and culture in the lives of the people of Chester and gives voice to their inspirations for the future ..." Another purpose was expressed, "If you ask Chester residents what they envision for a proposed Arts and Culture District in their downtown, they'll be the first to tell you that it's got to be Chester made, through and through." Walker evolved as a source of pride for the City of Chester. His origin and life story are the epitome of what a person can accomplish as a beloved human being and spiritual man. The docudrama was then featured by Butch.

The documentary was filled with jazzy music and exciting points concerning Walker's life. I was intrigued to hear once again what Wanisha thought as she expressed with tears, "He taught us how to be treated as young women just because of how he treated my mother. We knew what was acceptable and what wasn't, so I knew what to look for in a husband." Our youngest daughter Jaleesa explained this about her dad, "We appreciated what he did for us. He always made me feel safe and worthy. I feel like I deserve the best because he tried to give us the best." Our son-in-law Muhammad talked about Walker's humility, "We would watch sports together and because he was humble, I never knew what Walker had accomplished in football, basketball, or track. Whenever he would see me, he would get up and shake my hand. He was always there for us. Walker was always more interested in uplifting others by spiritually encouraging them." Our children openly expressed themselves on how much they loved, respected, and missed Walker. They saw how he walked through life in imitation of Jesus Christ who was taught to love, respect, and appreciate mankind by his Father Jehovah God even to the point of death.

The docudrama also shares the experiences of Walker's co-workers who considered him to be a "great guy." These words were part of Walker's reputation as Ron Hodge expressed after the premiere of the film. He explained, "He was always a gentleman to my wife and parents. Walker was always respectful. He's the type of a man that you would want your child to grow up with and to emulate and be just like. If you could have a son or daughter who was as good as Walker, you were doing okay for yourself. He was just a great guy. You could tell he was going to be a great family man. If you were just another person, he treated you with dignity and respect. He was just a great guy."

Gibson, a longtime friend of Walker's, expressed these sentiments, "I met Walker when he came to Chester High. I played with Walker at Widener as a freshman. We played football together. Walker was a lovable person. I only had one brother, but today I had two brothers and one of them was Walker. He was closer than a friend. Walker was the type of person that no matter whatever you asked him for, if he had it, he would give it to you. If he, had it, he would make sure you got it. You can't describe him in so many words. He was a person that I wish that I could have been like because he just gave and gave and gave. He had a spirit that he was not a jealous type of person. If Walker knew anything he could help you with, he was glad to do it. I appreciated I got to know him and play with him. Today I wish I could be the man that Walker was. He was a gentleman indeed." Gibson turned to both of our daughters and concluded, "I want you girls to know that your father was one of the best. There is no one better than Walker Carter." These endearing expressions made my heart as well as daughters rejoice. We knew these words were true because Walker tried to apply Bible principles and that's what made him the man that he was.

Walker's sister-in-law Robin Carter had so many cherished memories she revealed. Robin expressed how she admired Walker's especially as a great dancer. Her husband Steve would take on this smooth dancing role as a couple. I was thrilled to hear that. Walker's cousin Patricia Wesley also contributed encouraging words in his memory. Each of us had summed up Walker's life in a loving way. I reminisced about how I met Walker in high school. I loved Walker from the day I met him in high school. That love remains still. There was something about him that caused me to believe he would make a great spiritual head, husband, and father. I could see a God-fearing young man that first day that would evolve into an admirable man. Once he is resurrected in the new world here on earth in paradise, I would like to marry Walker again. A good friend of ours already promised he would conduct the ceremony. Only Jehovah God through his son Jesus Christ know the answer. I will await their response. Walker was da bomb! What a man.

Walker's Way is a book based on the true-life experiences of an imperfect man who looked to the real superheroes--our Heavenly Father Jehovah, and his precious son who gave his life for all humankind Jesus Christ. He is and was the "Greatest man that ever walked the earth." May each of us pray for that Kingdom Jesus taught us to pray for at Matthew 6:10. God's Kingdom will eliminate all corrupt governments that exist today and bring about true peace and love throughout the earth. Once again, that's a real superhero. Let's teach our children the truth based on the Bible about these real heroes. There is nothing fake or imaginary about Jehovah God's promises through his son Jesus Christ because God cannot lie as Numbers 23:19 states, "God is not a man, that he should lie, neither the son of man, that he should repent: hath he said, and shall he not do it? Or hath he spoken, and shall he not make it good?" (*King James Version*) We can trust and put faith in God's promises for the future.

This is Walker's family. The people he grew up with, loved, and admired.

Walker was taught by his parents to love and serve Jehovah God in harmony with the ransom sacrifice of Jesus Christ who gave his life for all humankind. Walker tried to live his life based on Colossians 3:10. "And have put on the new man, which is renewed in knowledge after the image of him that created him:" (*King James Version*) He taught these truths based on the Bible to his family and others as he walked-throughout his life. Walker "Baby" Carter knew he had to rely on Jehovah's holy spirit as an imperfect man to please God in his service to him and others.

Printed in the USA
CPSIA information can be obtained
at www.ICGtesting.com
JSHW072006131123
52003JS00016B/70